BOTVIN

D1282274

LEARNING BEFORE BIRTH

Every Child Deserves Giftedness

Brent Logan

Borvin

© 2003 by Brent Logan. All rights reserved.

Except for brief quotations in articles and reviews, no part of this book may be reproduced, stored in a retrieval system, or transmitted by any means, electronic, mechanical, photocopying, recording, or otherwise, without written permission from the author.

ISBN: 1-4107-4277-6 (e-book)
ISBN: 1-58820-231-3 (Paperback)
ISBN: 1-4107-4276-8 (Dust Jacket)

This book is printed on acid free paper.

1stBooks – rev. 7/22/03

*to our littlest ones
with the biggest future*

WORLD PRAISE FOR BRENT LOGAN'S
PRENATAL ENRICHMENT DISCOVERY

"Logan's work is redefining education, and is focusing our attention on perhaps the most important educational opportunity of all."

John Jarrett, M.D., Professor of Reproductive Endocrinology,
Indiana University and the University of Illinois,
author of *The Fertility Guide*

"This education wave of the future turns all parents' dreams into reality."

Malaysian Doctor, Kuala Lumpur

"A very important and innovative approach to child health and development."

Linda Duffy, Ph.D., Associate Professor of Pediatrics,
State University of New York at Buffalo, Executive Director,
The Women and Children's Health Research Foundation

". . . can help produce calm, contented yet highly responsive babies who are unusually physically strong and have an increased ability to concentrate."

Junior, London

"Logan's achievement is a giant step for mankind."

The Star, Kuala Lumpur

"For their child's lifetime benefit, every parent-to-be should hear about this discovery."

René Van de Carr, M.D.,
author of *While You Are Expecting*

"Uncomfortable births and unhappy babies could be a thing of the past."

Hospital Doctor, London

"A brilliant invention. I have used it myself, will definitely use it again, and have only positive things to say about it in my book."

Sarah Brewer, M.D., author of *Super Baby:
Boost Your Baby's Potential from Conception to Year One*

"Logan's argument is convincing."

Radio Times, London

"An idea of pure genius, one which the world will accept because it offers the most profound gifts for developing minds."

Mikhail Lazarev, M.D., Ph.D., Chief, Children's Health Laboratory, Center for Rehabilitative Medicine, Russian Ministry of Health, Professor, International Academy of Sciences and Art, Moscow

"Never mind the musical mobiles, baby rattles and lullaby toys, the ultimate in early learning is arriving."

Daily Express, London

"A noble and important advancement."

Mikhail Offengame, M.D., Director of Child Pathomorphology, Central Children's Hospital, Novgorod, Russia

"It's what every mother wants—a healthy baby who sleeps all night, who doesn't cry and who develops early."

Daily Telegraph, London

"It is hard to overestimate the benefits."

Roy Ridgeway, author of *The Unborn Child, Preparing for Parenthood,* and *Caring for your Unborn Child*

"Pushing the outside of the prenatal stimulation envelope."

Omni, New York

"There is a potential benefit . . . it could have a general improving effect."

Peter Hepper, Ph.D., Professor of Psychology, Queen's University of Belfast, Director, Fetal Behaviour Research Centre, Belfast, Northern Ireland

"Magnificent work."

Datin Noor Laily, M.D., Chairman, The Nury Institute of Family and Child Development, Kuala Lumpur

"...may eventually provide substantial health benefits for needy populations in developing countries. In fact, neurogenetic enrichment technology may also help to address a problem of public health importance in industrialized countries. There is a great need for efforts such as Brent Logan's, and we commend him for his commitment and dedication to this very worthwhile work."

Bill and Melinda Gates Foundation, Seattle

Contents

Illustrations

Preface

. . . an invisible doorway has been opened--a
doorway which, widening out, will take man
beyond the nature that he knows.

Loren Eiseley, *The Firmament of Time,* 1960

Whoever has raised children remembers the epic well.
From peer histories or our own early years, both good times and
bad can be recalled--often with amazing clarity. Nevertheless,
try imagining moments when youth distinctly differs from those
familiar portraits.

As opposed to a typically stressful start, this smiling baby
departs the womb relaxed, with eyes open; few if any cries
punctuate the delivery room. Birthweight and length are well
above average. Rather than briefly looking at faces or objects
like other newborns, it stares for many minutes, fascinated,
concentrating. Over merely days the happy infant adjusts to
sleeping throughout the night, rarely disturbing its parents.

Everyone notices an engaging alertness and curiosity. After
a few months words commence, compounding quickly into
simple sentences. Crawling, then walking take place early, with
unusual strength accompanied by precocious coordination.
Illnesses are infrequent, the minor malady readily behind.

Our industrious toddler not only learns fast, but playing
quietly alone or with anyone for hours merits a caregiver's
blessing. The child has surprising humor, yet always remains
kind. Among the abundant gifts, that which impresses most is a
talent for constantly helping others.

Once schooling begins, this gifted individual demonstrates
marked ability in each academic subject while maintaining
matchless social skills. Unlimited friends include those younger
as well as older. Teachers are dazzled by a depth of perception

revealing anomalous maturity and wisdom. Creative solutions to problems appear an easy exercise.

The childhood summarized above may strain not just belief, sounding farfetched even in an age when hyperbole is expected ...a myth no experienced parent would take seriously; yet, as the media report with compounding frequency, this narrative describes thousands of young people born worldwide to families at every socioeconomic level. They are radically changing many views about human nature, and therefore its potential: Because of their astonishing promise we can all enjoy an auspicious forecast, that optimal tomorrow today implores.

But, compared with the rest of us, these children commenced life by sharing an extraordinary sendoff ... *one which happened in the womb.* Welcome to where our future is born fortunate: the wondrous world of learning before birth.

What follows is the first account of a contemporary global phenomenon that begins during human gestation, an adapted enhancement raising consciousness past any evolutionary precedent. Readers will learn how the breakthrough means came about--from history to hypothesis, then theory, testing, and application--its beneficiaries in this instance children along with all they affect. If tomorrow has friends, these urgent words seek their stewardship.

The Descent of the Child, by Elaine Morgan, identifies a semantic vacuum:

> In an era of rapid social change two phrases have come into common use. There has been much talk of the New Woman, and only slightly less about the New Man. No one has yet begun speaking of the progeny of this couple as the New Child.

That telling omission is addressed by the book before you, its central thesis elementary yet perhaps obvious only through hindsight; nonetheless, an axiomatic example--in David Cohen's *The Secret Language of the Mind*--has confronted a quandary which leads past speculation:

…one of the key distinctions between the innate and the learned is that everything one is born with is innate. But if learning can start in the womb, it is much harder to make a clear distinction.

And from this discovery might an effective *practice* evolve? Educator Mac Freeman poses what ought to be the next question:

Maybe the common assumption that a fetus cannot learn is actually a result of fetuses not being taught?

No longer.

Acknowledgements

> . . . we human beings and all our tricks are
> just another product of the contemporary
> biosphere.

Daniel C. Dennett, *Darwin's Dangerous Idea*, 1995

Who truly solos? Even beneath superstructures gliding like metallic gods just shy of the stars can be found a few stolen struts, flight under the fullest moon still requires functional running lights, nor with turbulence ranging to thunderheads would this patchwork craft have taken wing save for favorable tail winds. Wittingly or not, help happened, in retrospect a conscientious conspiracy however configured. *Encomia!*

First, I am deeply indebted to those authors whose quoted passages afford diverse perspective--whether from science or art --on the themes which follow, newness needing any family it can find. Chapter Four's title originated with David Hickman, director of the same-named British television documentary (no less accomplished than his previous film, *A Brief History of Time,* about Stephen Hawking . . . who through the further physics of coincidence I recently met) overviewing my research, and narrated by actress Miranda Richardson. Hundreds of enthusiastic parents in a dozen countries contributed photographs of their children enriched before birth with the system I developed; it is unfortunate each charmed countenance could not appear here.

A phalanx of librarians repeatedly supplied references and tracked arcana: nonpareil sleuths Ginny Rollett, Tom Reynolds, Jonathan Betz-Zall, Kathleen McCluskey, and Cindy Lyons, Edmonds, Washington; Reita Fackerell, Seaside, Oregon; Dianne Hall, Oregon State University Kerr Library, Corvallis; the latter two--aided by Betty Jorquera Toro, Secretary of the Museo-Biblioteca Gabriela Mistral, Vicuña, Chile--located an exasperatingly elusive poem. To lend historical context, Kazue

Nakae offered her article on *taikyo*, Japanese prebirth practices, Hideo Fujimoto rendering an English version. I am responsible for translations not otherwise credited.

Countless professionals from relevant disciplines extended empirical assistance, among them: D. Raja, Vice Chancellor of Madras Medical University, India, supervised practitioner teams at four clinics assessing my technology through a multimodal, controlled study with 700 mothers; Sabaratnam Arulkumaran, Chief of Obstetrics and Gynecology at the National University Hospital, Singapore, confirmed in utero sonic parameters; Datin Noor Laily, Nury Institute of Family and Child Development, Kuala Lumpur, reinforced my findings with her own evaluations; Linda Duffy, Associate Professor of Pediatrics, State University of New York at Buffalo, and Executive Director of The Women and Children's Health Foundation, on several occasions graciously discussed standards for definitive measurements.

Superlative sonic engineer and jazzmaster, David Jones, Vancouver, British Columbia, adapted the womb's native music to a neurogenetic curriculum under instructions which would have sorely tried less dedicated or diplomatic technicians. Imparting ever reasonable and cheerful feedback, Sally Clegg--intrepid translator, planetary citizen--proved that peripatetic is an expansive project's perfect adjunct.

Seattle's Paul Hunter--poet, playwright, letterpress publisher, scholar, mariner, folksinger, polyinstrumentalist, longtime best if devilish advocate, word and soulsmith bar none--reviewed the manuscript for overly egregious discursive and linguistic slips; substantive errors (which nothing, natural or cultural, lacks . . . those random events behind emergent pattern) worse than omissible sins remain mine.[1] His always astute recommendation led me to the Robert Hass remarks on rhythm.

---

[1] Acutely embarrassing instances were assuaged by the logistical advice of physicist John Archibald Wheeler, quoted in Karl Popper's *Objective Knowledge*, "...make the mistakes as fast as possible," Jerome H. Barkow, Leda Cosmides, and John Tooby happily rationalizing: "...the first expressions of new and better approaches often look worse than the latest and most elaborate expressions of older and more deficient ones...."

Early encouragement came from Thomas Verny, Toronto; Peter Fedor-Freybergh, Stockholm; Sepp Schindler, University of Salzburg; Marian Diamond, University of California at Berkeley; Donald Shetler, University of Rochester, New York; Peter Hepper, Queen's University of Belfast; Susan Ludington, University of Maryland at Baltimore; Mikhail Offengame, Central Children's Hospital, Novgorod; Alfred Tomatis, Paris; Stan Gooch, Swansea, Wales; John Nichols, Guildford, Surrey; the late Roy Ridgway, Winchester, Hampshire; John-Richard and Troye Turner, Grotebroek, the Netherlands; Santiago Sanjuán Sanz, El Puig, Spain; Isabel Cantallops Fiol, Palma de Majorca; Chairat Panthuraamphorn, Bangkok; Melita Kovacevic, University of Zagreb; Phyllis Wilkin, Edith Cowan University, Perth; Ludwig Janus, Heidelberg; Ramona Negri, University of Milan; Beatriz Manrique, Caracas; Darold Treffert, Fond du Lac, Wisconsin; John David Garcia, Fall Creek, Oregon; Charles Laughlin, Carleton University, Ottowa; Leon Thurman, University of Minneapolis; and Sister Lorna Zemke, Silver Lake College, Manitowoc, Wisconsin.

Among the sounding boards who deserve unbounded acclaim for their constructive blend of resonance and dissonance are René Van de Carr, Hayward, California, indefatigable obstetrician, and another physician colleague, gifted musician, great heart, Mikhail Lazarev, Moscow, upon too rare opportunity sharing his prenatal insight--intact through immense struggle-- especially during an autumnal stroll along the River Volkhov in Novgorod where ineffable fancy met newfound fact, achieving a fulsome confluence (double luck, I later brainstormed nonstop with him to India and back, this book's simultaneous editing the stratospheric beneficiary).

Throughout his last years Hunter Williams, Seattle, lent a hand that belied burdens few could bear, and Richard Johnson, Lakewood, Colorado, friend over four decades, was always available for commiseration. Enormous appreciation is owed Gary Edwards, Indianapolis, for supplying 500 innercity mothers with my technology. Paragons of perseverance, Lisa and John Jarrett--Professor of Reproductive Endocrinology at Indiana University and the University of Illinois--likewise Philip

Broderick, all in Indianapolis, as well as Deborah and Michael Faigen, Lawrenceville, New Jersey, maintained morale at this end when the very overdue opus faced timid publishers or agents (one had me halve it, thus an allied volume pending).

My editor, Christopher Rennie, demonstrated the vision, verve, versatility, and viscera to take on more than even venerable veterans from the print wars could manage; additionally at 1stBooks Library, Lori Watterson, James Helsley, Joel Thomas, Michele Richey, Christian Kelly, Eric Kendall, Teri Watkins, Carrie Wilson, Melissa Maker, Candice McNeal, Patrick East, Anthony Potts, and Benjamin Jones spared neither acumen nor energy. As my final draft neared a putatively veritable deadline, the Puget Sound Tumor Institute's treatment staff was grand about letting me proof it while being irradiated daily for two months. Lest this list turn interminable in fact, no slight is intended to others affording me unmentioned support, their forgiveness solicited.

A life of spousal gratitude is owed Helga Bothe and Karin Müller; each anticipated an exemplary generation brought about by arduous, protracted labor, unstinting sacrifice--the pangs frequently seemed insurmountable--that momentous endeavor now bearing literally prodigious godparental rewards.

Finally, appreciation can never be sufficient for evolution's latest unfolding hereabouts, the advantaged children themselves, eager respondents once the womb (after hundreds of comparatively uninstructive millennia) made sense, and who surpass my highest hopes with delightful surprise.

Note

Learning Before Birth seeks a cosmopolitan audience--ideally of fetal influence--therefore more esoteric information is listed under technical references at the book's end, and should be consulted for those wishing corroborative data; still, somewhat complex subjects figure so germane to the subsequent pages they remain as ballast.

First came the cosmic infant . . . .

Rig Veda

Is not life before birth nothing?

Koran

Inside--there exists the family.

I Ching

. . . a child will show the way.

Isaiah

Chapter One--*Hidden History*

In the beginning . . . music.

Jaco Van Dormael, *The Eighth Day*, 1995

The universe positively *hums*, all matter obeying incessant rhythm . . . from atomic dance or cyclical seasons to the tempos of blood and brain. Even the immaterial resonates: Without pause, primordial starlight laps at us no less than immediate sunshine--natural or artificial--breaks in waves over this page. And the visible spectrum also creates mental art; how faithfully Marc Chagall practiced his colorful credo that "Everything vibrates," while the most farsighted seer, Olaf Stapledon, imagined an achromatic conceit that may yet prove genetic: "Man himself, at the very least, is music . . . ." Not a single instance remains silent to existential song which, among local members of the cosmic orchestra, humans both hear and play best: We appreciate or perform absolutely apart from other Earthlings, lately--born of necessity--taking to rather virtuosic improvisations upon the indigenous score.

Amplifying this deepest harmony, our lives follow tunes at every turn, outside and in, sensed or secret. Each behavior, thought itself, the sacred places once firmly identified as heart and soul--no feature affecting us (indeed, the entire realm evolution has bequeathed life) registers apart from order opposing its absence, the monolithic meaning behind knowledge which also shapes the unknown. Little wonder religions summon their adherents for worship with chimes, gongs, bells, or drums, while precipitating the transcendental intonation of prayer through hypnotic chants. Whatever the chemical response of body and mind, supplicants dearly embrace the psychodynamic effects these acts return. The holy must speak in melodious tongues.

Rites of passage--birth, puberty, marriage, accomplishment, death--receive predominately sonic veneration: Percussive

1

instruments typically mark the notable event (bloodline reinforcers like weddings incur joyous volume). In many societies, the moment when individual chaos first conforms to collective instruction--a baby's departure from the womb--is loudly observed. That patterning process--exemplified and espoused by our kind more than any other creature we know-- can describe the tribal welcome to life, often inferred not at gestation's end as in Western cultures but over the preceding months. From Papua New Guinea's Iatmuls to rural Madagascar, even less remote areas of contemporary Polynesia, Africa, and Asia maintain selective treatment or prebirth rituals where ancient refrains pulse a penetrating tattoo before pregnant mothers, some swaying with forceful footsteps into labor contractions or unmimicked delivery.

Influenced by the Confucian belief that fetal environment helps shape human character, 2000 years ago China institutionalized awareness of this stimulatory art, a sensitivity presuming the womb's protohuman possessed receptive and expressive powers; refinement in the prescribed techniques occurred during the late 1800s as the Quing dynasty was engendering a republic, with utopian recommendations comprising the *Ta-T'ung* (*Book of Great Harmony*), several notably eugenic. Wives were separated from spouses in bucolic settings, at tranquility clinics for repose and meditation under sage auspices; along with poetry or song, dicta about proper diet, cleanliness, and stress reduction were accompanied by gentle melodies from stringed instruments complementing mellow woodwinds.

About 1000 CE this heritage migrated to Japan, where on the streets of Tokyo today its name is still recognized--*taikyo*. Over the centuries, what had begun as a precaution--to ward off noxious spirits from the forming infant--was transformed by the tenor of successive times, superstition giving way to theistic interests then political pragmatism; gods could be propitiated if an unborn novitiate received proper counsel, venerating the emperor in advance. Finally, after World War II, a secular incarnation took place: Elevated to that status previously occupied by nobility or above, from national democratization and rising affluence children themselves became deified in all but name, an industriously enlightened generation gracing the Ginza, their parents mixing inherited though now vague notions with modern educational methodology. Attention directed wombward had acquired a scholastic slant.

If amalgamated in understanding or approach, contemporary Eastern prenatal practices have stayed not just positivistic but anticipatory: When pregnant mothers in Beijing, Seoul, and Taipei listen to popular tunes on radio or television, they are drawing from a vast cultural reservoir by sensing an experience presumably of mutual benefit . . . reinforced when their inner audience registers responsive movements. Other precedents promoting fetal intervention for postnatal value include mention in Indian texts from 100 BCE to 600 CE, also sixth-century Talmudic writings; by 400 CE the surgeon Susruta felt that an unborn child starts seeking sensation before the first trimester ends, its mind already extant five months from conception. Sage Vyasa--primary source for Sanskrit's epic *Mahabarata*, about 1500 BCE either compiling or authoring many of its 100,000 legendary and didactic couplets--was exposed in the womb to repetitive mantras, vedas, and slokas, a sonic backdrop directly connected by an entire culture with his reputed omniscience. But this awareness is no longer confined to one geography: A planet has been rather abruptly awakened by an altogether original rhythm--the music of earliest learning.

Save for scattered suggestions, Western history lacks much concern over gestational matters.[1] Now and then its philosophers mused on vibration as the cosmic cornerstone, Aristotle believing the fetus receptive to experience; however, their few

---

[1] Although not in native South America--most likely due to early Asian influence--as witnessed by the anonymous author of the 1767 *Journal of a Voyage Round the World in the Dolphin*:

> While a female Patagonian is with child, all disagreeable objects are kept from her; she is awakened by musick; they study to divert her with amusements most suitable to her taste; her mind is brightened with joy, without allowing her to grow slothful for want of action, she has exercise...as is most agreeable to her. The Patagonians do not doubt the mother's influence over the...constitution of the child.

remarks passed unappreciated by the populace in any apparent sense. Perhaps with mechanistic concentration upon the material, life other than that immediately evident seemed too ineffable, an abstraction disguised by a fleshly barrier which caused enough distraction to the intentionally mental.

Three exceptions: Comenius (John Amos Komensky), a seventeenth-century Czechoslovakian educational reformer who developed the first children's picturebook, proposed clinics for expectant women; about that time, British philosopher, John Locke, imagined fetal thinking receptive to external stimuli, while the German physiologist and founder of developmental psychology, William Pryer, also challenged an entire civilization's misperception by presuming, in *The Mind of the Child*, 1881, a prenatal precedent for the organ most prepared to teach itself:

>...we must be clear on this point, that the fundamental activities of mind, which are manifested only after birth, do not originate after birth.

But not until 1924 did professionals acknowledge in utero relation to an external influence, with that noted obscurely.

At Leipzig University, a less than elegant experiment was conducted by pediatrician Albrecht Peiper, who documented the gravid abdomen distending when its startled inhabitant kicked in protest to an adjacent automobile horn. After five or ten million years of maternal primate observation, science would at last report (in a barely circulating German journal) that the fetus could discern an ex utero occurrence; too frequently the self-evidence of profundities--what mothers since childbearing began had comprehended--eludes precisely those charged with their proof.

Apart from this little-noticed landmark, scant evidence of the womb-world connection exists outside the East save for certain Native and Latin American tribal chants or dances; following the Reformation expectant mothers across Northern Europe sang hymns while knitting together, a tradition fading after the mid-twentieth century. Further clinical comment on auditory response of the unborn child appeared sporadically: an incipient 1927 report by H. S. and H. B. Forbes at the University of Rochester; L. W. Sontag and R. F. Wallace, 1935; then a 1940 suggestion from David Spelt that conditioning and perhaps the crudest learning might describe fetal capability, his insightful inference extended through Donald Hebb's neurogenetic theories.

During the 1960s various postnatal tests under New York psychologist Lee Salk, brother of the polio vaccine's inventor, showed how a mother's heartbeat indelibly reverberates in the neurology of her offspring--an extraordinary finding yet one it would take another generation to prove advantageous. 1971 remarks by A. W. Liley finally made an impassioned case for the fetus as a person (concurrently, I was helping edit the first textbook sensitizing physicians and nurses to patient psychodynamics--especially when their charges were young or elderly--Anna Freud's point finally adopted). Its investigative pace quickening, the same period saw two professional societies form which recognized an emerging discipline of prenatal psychology, these groups holding regular congresses for disseminating views on their newborn field. The historical brake and accelerator are noted by Queen's University of Belfast researcher, Peter Hepper, in what might comprise a coming academic consensus:

> Because learning is central to human functioning there has often been a certain reticence to accept that the fetus is able to learn, as if in some way learning would lose some of its importance if present in immature organisms. However there is now much evidence that learning before birth is present throughout the animal kingdom.

By 1975, even at the popular level--as expressed by Mortimer and Lynn Rosen in *Your Baby's Brain Before Birth*--this awareness was beginning to define the nature of first cognition, with a hint toward controlled influence:

> If the fetus can respond, and, in addition, is in a state of development so that each response is more aptly called

5

learning, then indeed the fetus--in the broadest sense of the word--is learning prior to birth. This must be said cautiously, since we do not learn in utero in terms of $1 + 1 = 2$, or ABC. But perhaps marked environmental changes can shape later learning, ability, development and function of the fetal brain.

In recounting so brief a chronicle, what should appear astonishingly obtuse is that despite self-scrutiny born in Pleistocene times as the stamp of human consciousness, only now has *Homo sapiens* turned serious interest toward the moment when it starts becoming the paramount observer then practitioner of all life on Earth, examining the forces which affect its tender origins, and discerning how alternative influences upon our earliest development might prove collectively valuable; Plato's presumptuous philosophy was correct in one respect: "Whether works of nature or mind, their greatest importance lies in beginnings."[2]

Yet this complaint is comparative. Among these diversely endowed environs--rich with risk and reward--mortals constitute the learner species, and seen in epochal context knowledge accrues faster than mind can pretend interpretation, though perversely whetting appetite further. Faust would have sympathized with such industrious anguish: Impatience serves as a much maligned motivator, our chastised kind driven by systemic feedback to lead itself out of nonsense through lasting achievement, sense institutionalized.

Progress is realized as dream and frustration ever change places, why goals are met without remark while new ones materialize . . . yet from expanded appetite their successors

---

[2] Possibly also this strategist's confession: A disquieting legend persists that, as the foundation to Western thought was being laid, Plato himself burned preSocratic manuscripts, an ironic few nonlinear fragments from Heraclitus surviving; the late Carl Sagan mourned another early loss, the vast library at Alexandria, without which the Dark Ages might have been but passing shadows, Eastern wisdom nascently enriching European culture instead of the onerous task *we* face in reuniting a family grown global and gargantuan.

slightly needier, extrapolated undertakings for the replacement generation--which must have additional talents, improved tools, vaster horizons.   Heraclitus caught the universal dynamic incisively: We inhabit not fluid time alone but a space fixed in flux, neither shore nor streambed . . . except that, despite dangerously deceptive backwaters, with an inexorable force the cosmic river widens and deepens from our very swimming.

Chapter Two--*The Fetal Frontier*

Life's aspirations come in the guise of children.

Rabindranath Tagore, *Fireflies*, 1938

Like language, the genesis of tools (redated in 1997 to Ethiopia, 2.5 million years ago) derives from less and less random evolutionary pressures exhausting a momentarily uppermost niche of neural complexity, the same developmental process that has placed us atop Earth's sentient vector: From climatic or creatural crises, radical changes in environment-- inevitable challenge to natural selection's optimal edge--alter habitable zones, the annexed landscapes prompting new facility . . . thumb grasped the primordial stick which could defend territory, till soil, and etch our first glyph (this book created on computer an extension therefrom); just as bees signal and academic chimpanzees sign, birds use hooked twigs for grubs or rocks to open shellfish, otters--their sealevel bellies portable dining tables--the same, and primates secure termites with small branches, these all represent homeostatic pauses on the human journey, an upland perspective depicted by Stanley Kubrick in his breathtaking *2001* segue from hominid club to contemporary space station.

Along that causal chain of a dynamic becoming not just protective but preventive--taking the offense against possible injury--often with sudden thrust survival began to insist upon foresight replacing rear vision: Storehoused weapons could counter surprise, proximate crops meant less danger from foraging, history might teach by pictographs; an agreeable future born of energy and labor (muscular or technologized) would transpire through manifest investment.

And as the twentieth century matured, its scientific crafts continued their prophylactic success in medicine to look outside symptoms for the sources of human dysfunction. Initially, these were physiological, then characterological, not the least discovery being an intimate link--soon an equation--between the two; sociobiology proved a timely marriage of mind and matter, with its precocious spawn Darwinian anthropology, behavioral ecology, evolutionary psychology, and developmental psychobiology. We had started seeking causes behind human behavior, the connections between personality and performance; once identified, our attention turned to how those crucial sources could be influenced so that life--for individuals singly and together--might prosper beyond the present plateau. At the deepest level this search was indicative of an evolving group conscience, a moral argument Elaine Morgan has unswervingly mounted:

> The neglect or ill-treatment of babies arouses such pity and anger that it is hard to think straight about it. But after a child has been removed to safety and the perpetrators punished, it is still necessary to ask the human question "Why?" In what lost childhood did such callousness have its roots? At what point in the cycle of deprivation would it be most expedient for society to break in and concentrate more help and more resources? There is only one possible answer.
> At the beginning.

For in probing the uterine universe, trying to find reasons behind pernicious syndromes, investigation incidentally started detecting infant abilities where none whatsoever had been expected.[1] Real-time ultrasound, fetal heart or brainwave monitors, fiber optic color television detailing the first images of each growth stage--the resulting portrait revealed a sensitivity compounded by sensibility in the unborn child which stunned even staid researchers. This new catalog of proficient features dramatically defied the traditional Western prebirth characterization (much due to the Victorian attitude--clinically

---

[1] Similarly, researchers only now have discovered that female fertility describes a one-week monthly window rather than two--after 100,000 years since consciousness became capable of clocking pregnancy's onset, therefore its probable cause.

9

swayed by Freud--that young children possessed little else than an irksome, vegetal existence) while invoking potential the East had long intuited. Over but a few years professional suppositions fell before an amazing roster of elementary but undeniable *skills*, the genetically programmed repertoire--in concert with developmental openings receiving fit input--vast and vital. This revised procreational chronicle unscrolled like cuneiform deciphered.

No matter what motive induces its participants toward sexual union, the brutal or beautiful act of erotic congress is our foremost inherited compulsion, at root orchestrated by biologic necessity, bloodlines demanding replication in a hormonal juggernaut which formerly only physical energy and partner availability could modify; by contrast, we can also now enjoy that evolved love not always embracing the physical, priapic reluctance due to will expressing an *overlaid function*, mental descendant from the torrid crucible whence life struggled forth against initially stupifying but in time supportive odds . . . the collective kiss concurrent with civilization.

And microscopic lust mirrors this venerable organic mandate: Conception depicts an utterly turbulent battlefield, spermatic soldiers massively surrounding the hardly unreceptive ovum, its castle doors flung wide though battered from the steady if disoriented onslaught of butting heads, more population pressure than navigational skill, penetration being all were multiple admission possible (yet, as with Sun-Tzu's martial art, of late embraced by clever executives--required reading in the film, *Wall Street*--while the stalwart recess for second wind, a deceptive malingerer may sneak past). The number of spermatozoa generated for but a single egg's insemination is staggering; from an efficient engineering perspective, beyond one each would be redundant. However, elegance has never suited generic nature: Facing environmental hazard and defective mutations--Robin Baker's revelatory *Sperm Wars* reports one percent of pontential contenders are sufficiently motile for victory, the rest vicariously assist impregnation-- excess favors success in a reality constructed like an obstacle course (indeed, merely 500 million years after Earth's birth, the

10

human lineage started with chaotic slop, if not among tepid pondwater scum then by deep oceanic thermal vents, creation's messy though highly caloric soup kitchen, perhaps spiced by meteoric or cometary catalysts), so efficiency falls to increasing orders of awareness where in vitro fertilization currently crowns our inceptional craft.

Once triggered, genetically ordained cell division proceeds with the accuracy of an atomic timepiece; the minimally constituted embryo just days later starts shuttling information through its infant nervous system and a chemical network evolutionarily recapitulated as the "wet brain." The neurological engine is now engaged: By the third week cells congregate around an axis like a blueprint assumes that substance architecturally sensed, the neural tube our computer's earliest hardware--and mental processing of data supplied from visceral stimuli quickly begins. These first impressions may as a base include the omnipresent and overwhelming vibrations from maternal blood surging past, also initiation of embryonic heartbeat coincidental with the brain's groundfloor wiring; at four weeks this diminutive cardiac activity stabilizes from erratic bursts to its gestational rhythm of about two cycles per second.

Another week brings coordination of inner and outer worlds--stimuli registered bodily transmit with dispatch to the central terminal for rudimentary memory checks, filing correspondences or their lack as unknowns are compared against knowns; even erudite postnatal learning does not deviate from this procedure, education ever sequential, progressive-- epigenetic become curricular. But at two months from conception occurs the second most important event in our existence, a developmental extravaganza giving birth to all meaning. This explosion in neural material, its cerebral aspect identified as the first brain growth spurt, keeps detonating for ten weeks, producing cells at the phenomenal speed of 100,000 to 250,000 per minute--about half that generated throughout the body--representing a net gain since some parallel expiration is involved. Sure as a nuclear reaction, DNA messages precisely control morphology coordinated with developmental process and environmental persuasion, while what Stanford University

11

.

researchers term the *protobrain* is being constructed; its functions flourish at so rapid a rate that differentiated centers permit diverse bodily movements before week ten, the tiny corpus already gesticulating with arms and legs, twisting, turning, exercising. No feeble steerage, the fetal brain even by the first trimester operates surprisingly like that of an adult, its main features prefiguring their mature structure--irreplaceable elements laying those sensory and cerebral bases we obey over our duration, the years defined only from elaboration tempered with refinement.

If in the first weeks of life sonic waves start breaking on the preconscious shore by way of pressure fronts engaging the whole frame as though it were all ear (the interoceptive sense or autonomic system along with bone and tissue conduction relaying these signals), this phase before audition commences does not last long. Although reaction to sound has for many years been demonstrated from the fourth month, research no sooner fixes the onset of fetal hearing then earlier evidence is detected, now even before the twelfth week ends--as verified in 1991 by Peter Hepper and colleagues. During week twenty, captured visually as sonograms, the crying patterns of premature babies exactly match their mothers' speech--an impressive learning example, mimicry already a pronounced skill (at six months rare in utero vocalization from trapped air can startle outside observers). Classical conditioning, after the model of Ivan Pavlov's 1897 canine discovery, initiates with the human fetus at about six months.

Anthony DeCasper, University of North Carolina, documented this prenatal apprenticeship through an ingenious approach. Mothers in the last trimester regularly read stories aloud, and following birth their babies heard the same material along with new texts. By electronically monitoring sucking rates on pacifiers, he found that newborns favor the maternal voice over any others (1980), and keenest interest was expressed at those tales told wombside (1982). Since a fetus is more prelinguistic than the still speechless successor, infant recognition of verbal material to which it was exposed before delivery suggests broad discrimination in sonic packaging;

12

rhythms, inflections, intonations arranged singularly were the grounds for identifying what had been repeatedly ascertained earlier--even through an abdominal filter. By rights the gestational human could now be characterized as an avid listener, apparently eager for what makes modest sense, preliminarily yet technically educable--were germane teaching possible, perhaps a proposition no less preposterous than preschool seemed not many years before. Surely acute observervation led Moses Ibn Ezra to declare our aural dawnings "gates to the mind," and Voltaire felt them "paths toward the heart."

Should perception, remembrance, and an acumen for distinguishing between the two constitute prototypic thinking, then the question of degree arises. From young children and hypnotized adults, presumed prebirth or perinatal recall was first reported in the 1980s, with professional attempts at corroboration--music heard or played by the mother during pregnancy, a clattering scalpel in the delivery room. But family happenings not mythologized have a way of being subtly recounted, later persuading the previously hidden witness no less than questioner bias; like preconception history, extraterrestrial sightings or abductions, and assorted paranormal tales--reflecting natural phenomena, sensory errors, induced mental states, outright fraud, even psychopathology--upon rigorous analysis by less invested parties these accounts remain notoriously unsubstantiated, hard evidence simply lacking (this is not to discredit independent validation, sometimes the case with suppressed abuse memories). Only as experience increases from age do dimension and detail sharpen, accrued knowledge the determiner of content--why our earliest mental pictures remain diffuse, partially recorded, fragments contrasted with the fully fashioned lens we apply in vain attempt to piece them together. Amazing sophistication in the unborn child, past conditioning or habituation as experiments were shortly to confirm--but still within informed reason: Limits exist, even for the emotionally colorful fantasies of youth (like all faculties, the imagination must experiment--with exercise it stays vivid at life's senior end --so behavior can evolve).

This expanded caveat notwithstanding, thanks to press reports, word of newfound fetal competence was no longer esoteric; parents everywhere started talking about it, taking into personal enactment how they interpreted the message that the womb's occupant could after some fashion learn--and the curtain went up on a spectacular performance inside . . . followed by the eager birthlaugh of an enlightened Gaia in tiny guise.

Chapter Three--*Experimenting Parents*

Certain innovations appear to be almost
inevitable when evolution has reached the point
at which they become feasible.

Louis Halle, *Out of Chaos*, 1977

With that necessitous maternal instinct Plato identified,
novelty has the uncanny habit of meeting demand. Like an
energy field or critical mass created by interrelated activities
attaining a comprehensive changepoint, no sooner does
originality emerge than influence spreads and corresponding
developments follow--even in tandem, a synchronicity true for
the Cambrian proliferation of living orders[1] as well as Darwin's
immediate predecessors and isotropic cohort expounding
evolutionary theory. Beneath this phenomenon's magical
surface, of course, serendipity can be explained by covert
variables moving quantitatively toward qualitative sequels--
fossil evidence organically antedated, thought prefigured
anonymously. And our subject is similarly exemplified.

While color photographs in mass circulation magazines or
video glimpses increasingly revealed the womb--fascinating
fetuses caught at all formative degrees instructing us as no
school text ever had (though remarkably detailed wax obstetrics
models, displayed today at the Museum of Scientific History in
Florence, were available to Renaissance professionals)--the
1980s commenced with another advent. Before that moment,
recorded speech and music had been confined to mostly

---

[1] Geologically rapid though perhaps not the overnight event once thought
since new discoveries propose that precursory multicellular organisms
would have left little fossil evidence, being either soft-bodied or too
diminutive, with but minor DNA modification leading to major
morphological change.

15

unelected and immobile sources--radio, television, motion picture, public address system--with only the phonograph or reel-tape machine allowing listener options; sonic alternatives were at the mercy of someone else deciding content even if favorite stations or channels could be selected. But a single invention removed this restriction--suddenly and for good: The audiocassette player afforded portability, privacy, and the privilege of choosing only those sounds an individual wanted to hear.

Developed by Japanese industry in record time, over a matter of months Sony Walkmans invaded the planet--on streets, buses, trains, airplanes, in offices, restaurants, parks; bedrooms, beaches, and mountaintops became concert halls. Miraculously, the private world could transform its public counterpart--a visual disaster might take on the decorum of Corelli, boredom banished by the *bossa nova*. And if an expectant mother indulged dulcimer duets or the Beatles, what an intimate act to share her sonic selections with the family's newest member--*by placing earphones over the pregnant abdomen;* justification came as soon as her inner passenger began soft movements in rhythm to the same music she enjoyed.

This global phenomenon was extraordinary for originating under no powerful prescription, neither soapbox nor pulpit sanctioned the practice--it just happened. Simultaneously, the technological age that had brought to light the dynamics of human genesis now contributed the microchip . . . which concentrated electronics in a package mothers could comfortably employ for fetal access. And if not yet championing the innovation's secondary use, a few voices quietly encouraged its climate through groundwork or reinforcement.

By 1962 Ashley Montagu had summarized the body of growing knowledge under *Prenatal Influences*; a year later Albrecht Peiper's *Cerebral Influences in Infancy and Childhood* first saw translation, both volumes inferring that gestational life might be benefitted by judicious intervention. Shortly after, Shinichi Suzuki, conducting a world tour to promote training of preschool violinists, remarked on how classical selections might be played with favorable impact upon the unborn child. The

16

Sony Corporation founder, Masaru Ibuka, made a similar suggestion in his 1986 book, *Zero-Years-Old: Where Education Really Begins*; this pragmatic visionary also headed the Early Development Association, whose researchers had been broadcasting Japanese verse and songs prebirth (contemporary Asian expression of a traditional practice is further evidenced by the enterprising Sony chairman--recently deceased--Akio Morita, who followed my findings from 1989, as did the Shanxi Maternity Hospital, Taiyuan, China, beginning in 1992, already experimenting with fetal exposure to music).

But the ways families understood and applied this new information figured as various as character, ranging from caution to temerity . . . rarely methodical, often idiosyncratic; many seemed to have taken chapter and verse (also echoing B. F. Skinner) from John Locke's 1690 *An Essay Concerning Human Understanding*:

> . . . there are some ideas which we may reasonably suppose may be introduced into the minds of children in the womb . . . .

Not just music, but audiocassettes were played reflecting parental interests or desires for presumably likeminded offspring--sports, business, psychology, religion. Before, an instrumentalist with child might have dissociated their art from its adjacent listener, whereas now a populus of bellies was deliberately thrust against resonating wood, metal, or keyboard; cello, oboe, and xylophone became instructional tools attending this even earlier preschool. Kindergarten imports flourished, as mother, father, sibling, or grandparent intoned loudly toward their unborn target numbers, alphabet, colors, foreign languages.

In brief, the long Japanese transition of *taikyo*--from sacred to profane--was instantly abridged throughout the world: *A nebulous but committed intuition had realized that gains might result if special sonic attention were directed fetally*, Henry Ward Beecher's insightful maxim ("What the mother sings to the cradle goes all the way down to the coffin") applied at life's outset. This paradigm expansion in popular consciousness,

17

particularly parental perception, should not be underestimated. If a global generation decides to initiate novel behavior that defies the faddish by arising without advertisement, evolutionary factors could well pertain. No matter that the topical grasp was general, approaches scattered, articulating little in concert, or the outcome uncertain--brief, lasting, cognitive, social, physical, spiritual--a focus prevailed, and its expression involved place, time, means, purpose: the womb when occupied, external sound, and (whatever family entertainment might have inaugurated this inspired practice) *improvement* . . . the muted motive, pedagogy implied. Young parents whose lives had witnessed widespread socioeconomic progress replacing privilege and tragedy were strangers to the static; expressed like an earned right, they expected better for themselves--more so for their children.

However, this pervasive a secret could not remain solely public, and professionals began to take note. At the Eastman School of Music in Rochester, New York, Donald Shetler--who during 1965 with Shinichi Suzuki, on tour to promote his early violin training method, established that institution's gifted education program--was hearing how his pregnant students described movements of their unborn babies as proximate instruments were played. He recruited a few dozen to stretch headphones across their midriffs and focus thereupon recorded short selections of classic composers daily throughout the terminal trimester.

In Hayward, California, obstetrician and gynecologist René Van de Carr had for years listened while expectant mothers reported fetal responsiveness to sound or external touching. By 1984 an idea took shape and he formulated these actions as an applied program, detailed in his 1992 book, *Prenatal Classroom* (the 1997 revision is entitled, *While You Are Expecting*). To start, single-syllable words accompanied their manipulated actions on the pregnant abdomen--*pat, stroke, shake.* After repeated daily practice the infant might react with equivalent kicks to the pressure point, even duplicating the precise number when a command alone had been spoken--an impressively learned reply; later in term, this rudimentary lexicon extended its womb-specific vocabulary. As hundreds of families attended his

18

presentations, the method attracted international attention, and modified imitations began to appear; a few farsighted governments--like Venezuela, whose Beatriz Manrique spearheaded an effective prebirth project among impoverished neighborhoods--adopted Van de Carr's approach, with the Vatican paying considerable interest, and Singapore, where early education is encouraged, introduced a tax incentive to parents of bright children.

Yet while psychological benefits might reward a family intimately connected with their novice member, what could be said for genuine virtues afforded the child itself? How much of what was coming to be known as *prenatal stimulation* would actually pay off--not just claims from advocates, but empirically, measurable by the strictest instruments? In less than a decade, initial proofs were to see print--with meaning far beyond any text.

Chapter Four--*Brave New Babies*

All animal life is sensitive to environment, but of all living things the child is the most sensitive. Surroundings act upon it as the outside world acts upon the plate of a camera. Every possible influence will leave its impress upon the child, and the traits which it inherited will be overcome to a certain extent, in many cases being even more apparent than heredity. The child is like a cut diamond, its many facets receiving sharp, clear impressions not possible to a pebble, with this difference, however, that the change wrought in the child from the influences without becomes constitutional and ingrained. A child absorbs the environment. It is the most susceptible thing in the world to influence, and if that force be applied rightly and constantly when the child is in its most receptive condition, the effect will be pronounced, immediate, and permanent.

Luther Burbank, *The Training of the Human Plant*, 1907

Over the last century skepticism as that most sacred of premises underlying hard science has tightened its technique for testing veracity, scrupulous in intent and administration (though disguising frequent flaws): An innate mistrust subsides as anecdotes yield to pilot studies, these confirmed or denied by randomized, clinical trials--measured against a control group that represents the prevailing standard, and ideally self-suspect or double-blind to eliminate bias--with impeccable replicability the final test for jargoned "robustness." In the case of living subjects, duration becomes an evaluatory factor; longitudinality is expected if a favorable trait withstands aging--when precosity surfaces, aspiration to genius must demonstrate no provisional

20

claim. Should a cultural intervention before birth be alleged to foster long-term, even lifetime assets, the evidence may not remain hearsay or singularly observed: Multiple manifestations should disseminate through language and parameters expertise accepts.

When innovation in thought or its implementation comes about, development nearly always pursues a similar pattern: At first the phenomenon registers individually, then advertisement attracts degrees of confirmation, and these are dependent upon numerical endorsement according to identical protocols. So has transpired the ameliorating genealogy this book logs. The children Donald Shetler had stimulated during gestation were being described at four years of age as exceptionally talented in the arts, with musical ability most prominent among all subjects from his experiment.[1] While he exhibited academic reserve in public, privately Shetler did not stop at reporting giftedness for the group: *By various yardsticks prodigies had been produced.* Even so, the families involved were predominantly musicians, and although peer parents in the school but outside the project were bearing progeny exhibiting no like merits, postnatal environment became a detracting factor for suspicious educators --homelife included too many of the very skills these youngsters demonstrated.

Confirming Shetler's data, René Van de Carr could escape this criticism since the majority of children experiencing his approach came from diverse ethnicity and lower economic circumstances where music or other postnatal exposure to learning registered less than the norm. By 1985 he presented data before an Oakland conference of international physicians and psychologists: Controlled tests with newborns indicated rather significant findings from those fetally enriched, the first such announcement to any professional organization, shortly repeated at a San Diego congress. Published a year after with

---

[1] Which correlates with magnetic resonance imaging--by a team under neurologist Gottfried Schlaug at the Heinrich Heine University in Dusseldorf--showing the brain's hemispheric connector, the corpus callosum, substantially enlarged for sonic artists who received early training in the discipline.

psychologist Marc Lehrer, their information clocks the appearance of this research in print, documenting not immediate reactivity, as Albrecht Peiper had witnessed a half-century prior, but statistically lasting impact--at least for neonates and babies several months old.

One benefit depicted an infant's initial try at articulating a word, with another advance in actually saying it, early linguistic facility being shown by numerous researchers as predictive of later cognitive skills; ability to nurse could be considered an asset for the mother-child relationship, perhaps later psychodynamics and health (compare the propensity to smoking, where an oral element connected with premature weaning has been identified), and even paternal bonding profited. It seemed probable that an extensive phenomenon was taking place because physiological factors as well were involved, oddly the appearance of teeth (at one month following birth the average is only a single instance among 2000 infants, versus eight per 100 in the stimulated babies) . . . 160 times more than usual! Though preliminary, these intriguing outcomes--where Van de Carr's verbal/tactile procedure had been applied--argued persuasively for further investigation.

Soon, lending support as the first wave of prenatally stimulated children matured, observers besides family, friends, neighbors, or awestruck strangers began to comment: Obstetricians, nurses, pediatricians, educators, and psychologists confirmed a growing picture of exceptionality. While not every beneficiary exhibited *all* superlative traits, a degree of facility at an elevated level identified each, with this proficiency tending toward multiple presence in the person; taken together, the reports resonated quite unlike those from randomly selected collections of infants lacking fetal intervention. Despite a common sonic denominator, it was as though the inconsistency in approach--methods mirroring parental interpretation--had produced precisely the wide variety of attributes being witnessed. Yet no matter which technique, relative value was the reward; following is a composite portrait.

If patterned sound beyond maternal and fetal heartbeat had reached the womb as soon as the first few weeks after conception, mothers were indicating their baby's initial stirring--that proverbial quickening so viscerally felt--appeared a month early. Contrasting short, erratic, and sometimes violent responses to sudden external noise by quickly habituating--a startle reflex replaced with acceptance or endurance--these infants commenced softly repeated limb activity for considerable periods accompanying musical exposure; variable in effect were selections from the classical European masters where evenly measured tempos prevailed (of course Mozart, but also Vivaldi, Brahms, Schubert, and Strauss).

Were earphones employed over the womb, a fetus would typically situate its head near one acoustic source or the other; moving speakers to different abdominal locations on the mother sent the infant in rapid pursuit. Some relieved recountings indicated that breech birth had been averted as the desire for sonic proximity was used to deliberately somersault babies into the birth canal by methodically lowering this musical inducement during the last hours before labor commenced.

Delivery itself further defined the prenatal stimulation factor, clearly contrasting our traditional entrance. Although physically, emotionally, and psychologically liberating to the mother, the ultimate release is attained at painful price; whatever the extent of preparation or subsequent joy, parturition has always been described by the adult participant and witnesses in unflinching terms--if honest, no one minces words about not wishing an instant replay, while rationalization may take many years, sometimes never. Even among hazy claims from those traveling back under hypnosis to fetal or perinatal perspective, none reports unbounded bliss--only causist historical revisionism revisits Eden; despite any subsequent traumata, on the caricatured psychiatric couch resides a starkest reality, and that is the exorbitant cost of being born: For our initiation ceremony to the world, in one way or another we pay until passing from it. If so applied, Robert Frost's anguished wartime quatrain accurately captures this seminal stigma:

> A voice said, look me in the stars
> And tell me truly, men of earth,

23

If all the soul-and-body scars
Were not too much to pay for birth.

A typical neonate emerges from the intensely pressured journey demonstrating total resistance to the new, frame stiffly defensive, hands clamped shut, arms and legs squeezed tight to the body, eyes fighting bright lights, lungs shuddering into function, voice testing parental hearts with that baleful wail caregivers insist signals vigorous health--the human condition rudely met through another generation's instant rejection. Yet the fetus whose background included environmental enrichment in a sonic vein starts quite otherwise, with seeming insight about their daylight debut--an element of preparation appears responsible for demeanor traditionally unknown.

Beginning with an almost anticlimactic entrance, pliability epitomizes both this unique newborn's corpus and character: It flexes with--rather than resists--the constricting birth canal, arms and hands limber, facilitating not fighting; this may account for the shorter-than-average labors. No rage against light's dawning, the immediately curious infant squints, adjusts its visual aperture, and lets the sunshine in--widest stares or frequent smiles greet the assembled faces--beaming acceptance. With like openness, steady and strong breathing absorbs surrounding sustenance rather than exerting panicked ego to brush the universe aside; nurses may assume the worst, that crying must occur to clear occluded lungs, but the child's behavior reveals not the slighest indication of stress. Buddha's reputedly quiet and open-eyed arrival may bear relevance, as might the Christian nativity legend.

Humans at birth typically gaze upon objects or people for the fewest seconds, while their prenatally furthered counterparts linger many minutes over the same scenery, even if detail is sacrificed for less than perfect distant vision[2]; a probing analysis

---

[2] Past genetically coded nipple range, neonatal sight discriminates only edges marked by high contrast, the boundaries separating dark from light-- why black and white shapes best serve our earliest optic education, an observation commercialized through numerous infant products developed

24

extends sensitivity, experience compounding exponentially instead of arithmetically--just as premature learning transpired faster in utero. And with audition the difference is similarly striking: Parents are flabbergasted when the baby swiftly pivots its head upon first hearing its mother's or father's voice, holding that dedicated pose as though finding their speech patterns thrillingly familiar; did the additional acoustic training alert formative fetal attention to other prevalent sounds penetrating the womb?

But this worldly bravura is not restricted to the senses alone: Newborns with a stimulated history exhibit substantially advanced body coordination, on occasion neck and shoulder strength sufficient to support unassisted their inquisitive heads, at times independently sitting upright with umbilical cord still attached. Stethoscopes and instruments have been grasped firmly enough that physicians must pry them loose finger by diminutive finger. Just outside the uterine terminus, mature expressiveness is also evidenced vocally, with infant instances of delight or even laughter enlivening a saga less and less anomalous.

One might propose that these breathtaking babies--by sheer extension of proficiency at a developmental stage as yet mostly pristine from the ex utero environment--further an argument advanced among more audacious professional circles, namely, that identity bears a rigorously indelible stamp from the start, either genetic,[3] prenatal, or both . . . but so preliminarily embedded it will not diminish throughout the organism's life; should this thesis hold for all vertebrates or primarily with primates is an academic dispute less important than its

---

under Susan Ludington, Professor of Maternal and Child Health at the University of Maryland School of Nursing in Baltimore, and many others since.

[3] 1998 Israeli detection of a gene which might determine newborn alertness could confirm such major temperamental incipience, while Robert Plomin (see M. J. Chorney *et al.* in this book's technical bibliography) discovered what may prove the genetic connection to intelligence--perhaps influencing fetal nutrition--a possible test for prenatal enrichment's effectiveness, even its heritability (as my companion volume discusses).

25

immediately applicable human meaning. Whatever panoply of behavior our kind exemplifies, a division between opposites--indistinct at midpoint yet palpable in the extreme--defines how we treat ourselves, other creatures, and the planet presently accommodating us.

Naturally, besides delineating actions, these polarities fashion ideas and emotions, labeling character correspondingly, cleaving constitutions: introvert or extrovert, conservative or liberal, sapient or sentient. In short, the net *politics* of personality, despite disparate traits within the individual--the thrifty freethinker, benevolent dictator--fundamentally looks either over the shoulder or horizon, past opposed to future; it fears or welcomes, offers fist or hand (etiologies of right and left have been brilliantly elucidated by John David Garcia, his latest exposé being *Political Ethics*). Detectable in the child and unchanging throughout their lifespan, this is a Rorschach of the soul many suspect without voicing, the socially unacceptable stigmata we secretly and steadily solicit, shaping our hatreds as much as loves, commanding where stones or votes are cast.

What truly fascinated observers about newborns enjoying sonic stimulation before birth, however, was that they could be readily categorized under the overriding behavioral morphology of *access*, not dismissal . . . an infant who in broadest terms seemed to receive greater pleasure from giving rather than getting, a generic attitude followup studies would reveal age only accentuated, their *emotional quotient* (EQ) prodigious. The combined features of prolonged looking, peaceful demeanor, outgoing mien, keener sensitivity, and instant responsiveness inferred an empathic frontier, a border discriminating the core makeup, had been crossed--imparting directed momentum.

Fear is believed to surface within the first weeks after birth, when elementary memory allows experiential comparison; by then enough pain has registered, in extent or repetition, so that any reappearance evokes avoidance as the senses try apprehending its telltale shape, defensiveness early learned for survival (although newborn chicks fleeing a hawk's shadow--and no other--indicates how genetic predisposition sets one creature respectively trembling). Yet if prenatally enhanced babies were

26

not recoiling from objects or occurrences typically frightening the uninformed, what could account for this uniform mettle? Did the recurring precedent of pertinent patterns stabilize formative neurology, organizing chaos, sharpening environmental appreciation, advancing data-gathering to expand maturity? By inaugurating an aggrandized scope of human output, were infants exiting the womb effectively older, demonstrating a mental grasp along with that correlated sophistication previously impossible except by neurogenetic accident--not at all abbreviating childhood but actually amplifying it? If true, the implications from this extensive a transformation were little short of headspinning.

Since introduced in the 1950s, Western hospitals administer the Apgar test at one and five minutes following birth, a measurement designed to detect neonatal problems. On this scale where 10 ranks as the optimal number, many facilities are reluctant to award much more than midrange--if crying is assumed indicative of good health, even psychology-- conservatism being the medical community's Hippocratic hallmark (supported by a not surprisingly affluent insurance industry). Ordinarily, the earlier score starts lower, with advancement to an acceptable level signifying the newborn as ready for subsequent procedures. Therefore, when ratings of prenatally stimulated infants invariably achieve the top mark, physicians and nurses take uncharacteristically astonished note (also true in Asian delivery rooms where other evaluations are applied); consistently launching attentive, cheerful, and robust if sonorously reserved children--into a world fraught with systemic hazards hence favoring such traits for survival--makes the obstetric community insistent upon knowing why.

But of the first statistics, those starkly outstanding were the sonically experienced babies' dimensions: Birthweight and length--irrespective of parental size--averaged among the highest, with a significant proportion in the uppermost one percent; also, cranial circumferences measured noticeably larger . . . without elevating the caesarean rate, which is instead substantially reduced. While these infants hardly appeared huge, the fact that they were not inconsiderable never seemed a family

27

concern (even proving an enviable feature among cultures where stature--compared with norms for countries nutritionally affluent--has become a status symbol, one of natural selection's latest expressions), especially since smallness attending prematurity may indicate lifelong deficits . . . from IQ and attention span to eyesight or behavior.[4] An obvious explanation might be that greater physical activity of the fetus syncopated to ex utero stimuli, where bodily exercise elevates oxygen or other chemical levels in the brain which promote growth factors. Most intriguing was the suggestion that cerebral matter had been so elaborated--through ways later research would detail--its volume required a slightly larger housing . . . despite science's disregard for older studies examining similar differentials, including those contrasting humans and their primate predecessors; this explanation underscores new evidence comparing the average cranial capacity of lawful society with measurements from hardened felons, in addition to reports indicating that neuronal plenitude defers mental decline among the elderly.

Yet how to account for the generally abbreviated labors--a few hours shorter than average? That the incidence of breech deliveries was reduced--because infants had been situating their ears near the sonic source, and followed late in term as speakers were lowered toward the birth canal--might have relevance, but no doubt maternal perceptions played a role: Mothers involved daily for many months in an in utero practice evoking equally patterned fetal response could scarcely be oblivious to the possibility of favorable effects, perhaps registering their anticipation hormonally, even physically, with relative relaxation a perinatal factor. And did that overall *willingness* noted in the brave travelers themselves, an early courage born of apparently insatiable curiosity accelerating by gestation's end, prompt venturing headfirst as process *participants*--rather than mere

---

[4] A National Institute of Child Health and Human Development study in 1998 under Mary Hedigar connects low birth weight to adult obesity, diabetes, heart diseases, along with chronic illnesses, while a 2001 British investigation by Marcus Richards *et al.* demonstrates that heavier babies and higher intelligence are related.

products--to a new domain where clearer sound and light beckoned, outgrowing not just physically but characterologically the old world both womb and past culture represented? These speculations would take on purposeful substance once a consistent trail of derivative benefits was established for increasing numbers.

That remarkable record commenced with a range of key differences from typical infant traits. Beyond the extraordinary alertness, focus, size, health, strength, and calm disposition noted neonatally, factors like ease complemented by extent of breastfeeding pertained--again, René Van de Carr the first documenter--even significant finger and toenail growth. Yet perhaps the leading indicator of giftedness was quickest to distinguish itself.

Unlike the prenatally advantaged--who almost seemed not to mind--traditional babies exit the birth canal with earsplitting remonstrance, distressed by the physical discomfort accompanying their tortuous transit, and painful appreciation of an environment whose sensory bombardment may only slightly exceed the womb in loudness but is still overwhelmingly alien, no longer filtered sound or light. Past the customary disdain at this shocking moment, typical newborn linguistic skills remain extremely limited variants of voluble frustration or fussy whimpering, their sonic repertoire confined to a developmental heirarchy which evolves in strict sequence. Throughout the 1980s, as tape recorder and then video camera began to capture the language ladder for various species, specialists could see that in humans the prevailing characterization of early vocal activity being little more than noise was wholly incorrect: Syntax and grammar would follow, but infant sounds made definite sense.

For example, the visual rendition of neonatal clamor produces a sonogram or "cryprint" that precisely duplicates the rise and fall of maternal speaking; during pregnancy, a mother's voice, notwithstanding how cadenced or inflected, becomes the singular template shaping each syllable of her offspring's acoustic repertoire, as though an instrument tuned by sympathetic vibration. This fascinating reconstruction of where and how we acquire our theme song constitutes persuasive proof

29

that the womb's sonic environment can with fetal learning form subsequent expression.

Further, these orchestrated melodies evolve through universal levels: However much vocal variety is present, babies worldwide croon an identical tune--starting with the broad vowels of cooing. Over the initial weeks after birth, infants earn their name: The Latin *infans* means those incapable of speech, identifying a neonatal lack challenging parents eager for spoken communication. But between crying spells newborns begin losing that limitation by first emoting the soft tones of pigeons, gently modulating breath to discover a self-contained instrument; the small mouth experimentally moves air back and forth, elevating low hums to an art. Then, weeks later, a hesitation toward the throat's recesses truncates this open sound with guttural utterance--technically known as the *ah-goo* stage. With little variance, subsequent months bring on a cascade of repeated consonants--*buh-buh-buh, tuh-tuh-tuh, duh-duh-duh, muh-muh-muh*--before coupling the earlier vowels to elicit every parent's pride at the elocutionary instants inaugurating *mama* and *dada*. Soon thereafter one noun meets a second, an adjective or verb appears, and the swift climb to simple sentences progresses. Mayan or Malay, farmer or physicist, unimpaired humans commence reporting on--and demanding from--their new cosmos identically.

Though the speed and scope with which this operatic facility is undertaken remains constant, retardation demonstrates less just as prodigiousness enlarges the range. And it was in language acquisition where prenatally stimulated babies repeatedly broke records; if educators were becoming convinced that the ability with which information is digested by the developing brain-- receptive and expressive functions--accurately predicts accomplishment over a lifetime, then milestones were being passed with historic precedence. The former gauge of potential had considered those points at which creeping, crawling, toddling, and walking start--or visuo-spatial abilities--to indicate a child's later success in primary skill areas. But hearing and speaking, the world analogized through words, were being held as more precise expectations of where the mental computer's hardwiring would commit that creature in which experience is elevated to an art. The repeated fact of prenatally endowed infants shedding their mute demeanor months earlier than expected, assembling a catalog of named people and objects at twice the conventional rate, stringing together sentences well before their first year--frequently with complex constructions that reflect astute analytical powers--began registering an inescapable conclusion among parents who consulted professionals to verify the phenomenon: Listening or talking better were those calipers by which social relationships, scholastic performance, and employment rewards were measured in adulthood, toward which certain children were making extraordinary strides.

Even the older assessments were signalling a substantial change: Hand-eye coordination, refined motor movements, standing erect and balancing, taking an unassisted first step--all happened months before their appearance in peers nonstimulated fetally. Whether limb activity brought on by the additional sonic presence prebirth, or neurological enhancement affecting sensory perception and bodily response, a mature physicality--deft as that of considerably more developed youth-- engaged everything consciousness could confront, complementing an insatiable cortical resource.

Instead of slavishly purchasing the latest overpriced and soon discarded toys, families were marveling at how imagination worked to occupy for hours these independent minds. A scrap of paper, discarded cardboard box, sand or grass no different than anything else taken for granted by throwaway societies became an instant but veritable universe for sight given to insight. Better yet, siblings and playmates received undivided attention from purposeful regard as it fulfilled the ideal role model's function; muting ego's first martial arts, exemplary negotiation was calming neighborhoods where cacaphony and bruises had immemorially reigned. When viscerally encountering this enchantment, cynics were equally swayed.

Printed word recognition constituting elementary reading-- sometimes as soon as eight months--was a precursor to early school entrance and superior academic achievement invariably

31

inviting the compression of grade levels; university admission more than a few years before usual was not uncommon. While private education could with smaller class size enable less-pressured teachers to nourish individual strengths, average test scores of fiscally fortunate but fetally unstimulated students registered lower than those from prenatally benefitted youth enrolled in public institutions. Scholastic assets from superlative intelligence initiated before birth were serving inquisitive minds to optimal adantage irrespective of their postnatal milieu: If the environment afforded comparatively less, compensatory curiosity, stamina, and perspective could more than address this deficit. IQ centered around 150, with significant instances in excess of 200--despite family history or economic status, which was typically unexceptional--a stirring new measure for intellect.

But besides brilliance and kindness, the creative element also shone with stellar accomplishment, an incredible agility of response in problem-solving, proffering fresh answers to timeless questions, making simple the long difficult yet sufficiently penetrating so that implications derived from even the ordinary did not escape. The number of impressive young artists, writers, and musicians (whose success depends dearly upon temporal awareness complementing tonal recognition--both attributes perhaps prenatally attuned) described an energetic concentration unknown to any culture; since their disciplines are those which sense hence shape what soon transpires at the popular level, an upwelling of futurists had been loosed upon a world too often mired in the romanticized past and only marginally contending with its problematic present. As premonitory as the obliterating final image from Peter Weir's apocalyptic film, *The Last Wave*, so towering loomed this tidal surge of industrious talent that it held every prospect for unleashing the very flood needed to wash clean a terrain cluttered with monuments celebrating victories which no longer mattered; once accomplished, the time could come for global regeneration, ecologically granting Gaia her due while constructing the moral society John David Garcia espouses.

Through anecdotes leading to proofs, should this pertinent intervention by parents into the lives of their unborn children

32

continue demonstrating systematic and durable gifts as substantial as the talents already conferred, then indeed culture could be claimed a reliable evolutionary checkmate for inordinate environmental demands: those from the world we have engineered, and that infinite realm into which our constructive activity is thrusting us. Humans entering the contentious third millennium are being equipped with the mental armament for waging a war against demographic and informational overload while displaying an unprecedented altruism--what John Fowles' masterwork, *The Aristos*, identifies beyond narcissistic id, ego, and mediatory superego to be our self-denying *nemo*--herald of consciousness advanced lightyears from its predecessor.

Chapter Five--*Novel Neurology*

> How could centers governing new and unusual functions arise in the cortex of the human brain if they were not previously located there? The answer apparently is that the brain is astonishingly plastic . . . . It is tempting to speculate that this plasticity leaves room for further evolutionary improvements . . . .
>
> Theodosius Dobzhansky, *Mankind Evolving*, 1962

Fact: A needy species has given birth to rapidly increasing numbers of children who from earliest enrichment are demonstrating significant advances in all performance categories. *Question*: Why is the prenatal period of *Homo sapiens* so important for introducing these benefits? *Answer*: Potential figures prominently even in this paramount primate's initial brain structure--its remarkable morphology facilitating functions no other life on Earth displays--and how it becomes organized.

A simplified illustration explains: Envision two neurons, both serving as terminals which store and transmit information. If a single conduit connects them, conveying electrical impulses between though allowing only unidirectional flow, then, before commencing, every message (hypothesized as an *engram*) must pause until preceding traffic attains its destination and the reply is acknowledged. But, were a second conductor available, while one signal is being routed to and returned from the target, another could adopt parallel or opposite transit--doubled efficiency, 100 percent speedup (in *Santiago theory*, the contextual dimension strengthened). Just this complexity-- additional sites, linkages, or both--distinguishes extended mental alternatives and abilities; evolutionarily, behaviorally, Louis Pasteur's 1854 maxim applies to generic neocortical history

34

along with the discovery discussed here: "Opportunity opens for the ready mind." In an inelegant but accurate comparison, more upstairs plumbing implies a commodious home surging with utility, no underfunctional hovel . . . until accommodation once again gives ground before aggrandizement.[1]

The saddest pathology resides in that impoverished neural network defining a retarded person's brain, where huge lesions punctuate or tiny tunnels riddle its tissue, vacuums representing ghost functions; the etiolated landscape features fewer cells, stunted junctions, decreased ducts, shorter and thinner roots, absent branches, unsheathed cables . . . pathetically less biochemistry--the etiology of autism, attention deficit disorder, depression, mental degenerative disease. Thus it should not surprise us to find that individuals so jeapordized cannot compete with those free of cognitive impairment or empathic inertia, whose choices remain unfettered, where minds and actions are at optimum capacity for the host species.

Some neoDarwinians may underplay progressive analogies, but ultimately there is no escaping that cortical sophistication with attendant growth in awareness--permitting their very conservatism its inherent contradiction--marks successive steps up history's helical staircase, and the reason we dissect or deify the rest of nature (rather than it practicing a reverse regard, which all subordinate life suffers) is due to our rarified legacy, an exotic if at times vain neurology conferring epic privilege. Why severely deficient members in our otherwise lucky clan exhibit froglike responses to stimuli is because their guidance system tragically resembles that of amphibia--elementary construction inadequate for elaborate tasks; when damaged, machinery adapted in a species for elevated operations reverts the owner down stairs ascended over planetary eras. This cruelest inheritance taxes the proximate relatives' emotion,

[1] Like overworked computer imagery explaining cerebral dynamics, crudely contrasting the Santiago model, mechanical analogies remain imperfect--as well as ironic when artifacts are employed to describe our nature or activities--yet this approximation devalues metaphoric power scarcely less than words disserve their meanings or art distances reality, instead focusing consciousness.

stamina, and economy . . . as well as the compensatory services of concerned communities, striving to reinforce the mores defining them; although emphatically no call for retroactive eugenics, a deeper understanding of neural origins is at minimum merciful--with an emphasis upon how they can be upgraded.

While the human male brain averages ten percent greater volume compared with the female organ (which in several of its regions contains additional nerve cells), size or density alone are not absolute factors responsible for intelligence and a corresponding independence from genetic constraints; yet these gross aspects count more than other cortical contenders in critical categories like *encephalization*, where the cerebral-corporeal ratio contrasted with that of a creature similarly scaled reveals an indisputable difference--the comparative dimensions of our heads, outside and inside, set us quite apart. A revealing report by R. O. Fisch *et al.* found that bright seven-year-olds possessed large cranial measurements at an early age; mental morphology, with characterological impact, according to Susan Ludington, exemplifies "a direct reflection of the number of brain cells and the density of the dendrites." When it comes to the brain, bigness in a given body is everything--and for these environs we are the prominent neural oddity.[2] An exhaustive 2000 analysis by John Wickett, Philip Vernon, and Donald Lee could not express my point better: "There is no longer any doubt that a larger brain predicts greater intelligence."

From a behavioral perspective, new studies--echoing David Wechsler's comment on psychopathy two generations before-- compellingly correlate criminality with reduced cranial dimensions, ultimately authenticating sociobiology by technique, tomographic or functional resonance imaging the latest tools. If those considerations which encourage individuals to share gainfully in groups--stout stitches for the civil fabric--are directly derivative of neural sophistication, then to counter present global

---

[2] One highly publicized attack on nineteenth-century phrenology contrasted the accomplished pate of Russian novelist Ivan Turganev with that of his French counterpart, Anatole France, the former 50 percent more than average, the latter much less--which only illustrates that all rules include exceptions.

fragmentation the singlemost resource soliciting emergency assistance is plain. This finding mirrors recent detection of congruency between dementia, principally schizophrenic, and skull measurement along with structural differences like larger fluid-filled cavities; broadly speaking, smaller cranial girth or diminished areas therein imply that positive cultural interface has less chance--producing grossly internalized effects, a delusional distance to reality paralleling the close correlation between lesser head size and Alzheimer's disease confirmed in 1994 by Amy Graves.

Regard our antecortical circuitry: We were programmed while inhabitating a rapacious environmental niche· for rapid engagement or departure, the ferocious fight or fearful flight syndrome of rawest survival (and why the night's first dreams tend to threaten, those necessary battle rehearsals suppressed upon waking lest they interfere with diurnal reality). But when Goliath's shadow now appears, our fate can be determined with other than extremes like raging or running. Anyone who has worked the mental wards knows with guarded intensity that distraction from obsessed intent--humor or self-effacing feint-- helps defuse volatile situations. Similarly, discourse replacing discord speeds teams of negotiators with degrees in graduate diplomacy, and experience authenticating their skills, to sites where bloodshed threatens: Humanizing an enemy not psychotic (though R. D. Laing's heroic approach suggests clinical categorization assures its very enactment) prevents worse, with persistence usually gaining a friend.

Warlords and recidivistic felons have been inextricably cast in their ravening roles by physically diminished neural capacity--any contrast with polarized positions remains less conceived should information access be naturally constricted. But if multiple choices stem from the richer cortical resource-- extra memory, faster answers, refined feeling--then jails and military graveyards may vanish. Contemporary science has broached a genetic basis for pathological behavior, yet the bellicose bloodline might be held at bay if not overridden were our earliest surroundings to engender empathy as the best selfishness, victory redounding to the xenophile.

A concept Darwin entertained for groups, which Robert Trivers in 1971 fleshed out individually--also explored by Lionel Tiger, lately David Sloan Wilson and Elliott Sober--is *reciprocal altruism,* where concealing even Machiavellian motive can pragmatically achieve the greatest number's good, contrived conscience preferable to none; over minimal time and easily tested, kindness proves infectious . . . artificial grins actually trigger biochemistry elevating mood, the happy face prosthesis restoring from an average few a day for adults the hundreds of smiles most children radiate during hastened dawn through delayed dusk (conversely; the late novelist Ken Kesey has written a fable emphasizing the observation of Franklin Roosevelt that fear is its own source). Such an Elysian outlook derives from none other than the basic mechanisms of mentation; note Walter Freeman's defining causality:

> Consciousness may well be the subjective experience of this recursive process of motor command, reafference and perception. If so, it enables the brain to plan and prepare for each subsequent action on the basis of past action, sensory input and perceptual synthesis. In short, an act of perception is not the copying of an incoming stimulus. It is a step in a trajectory by which brains grow, reorganize themselves and reach into their environment to change it to their own advantage.

Is this not why--slavishly implementing genetic law, that ingrained command to maintain at any expense the standardbearer--we consciously (or not, dreamstate prolepsis) suppress negative memories while exaggerating present problems, prefer lurid headlines over too proximate vicariousness, beaming bravely past the cemetery of real or imagined dangers? In a progressively perverse sense, genes are monomaniacally self-preserving, even to the point--culturally expressed--of preferring for the human puppet fixed creation myths rather than face their own truly fluid nature: They *must* be aggressively opportunistic; evolution simply had to happen because static security is inadequate for overcoming what might become--despite every calculation--more than insignificant threats. As will be seen, when applying the above quote to our hypercritical window of neurogenesis, with the divisive, biologically narcissistic edge now blunted by an unstoppably homogenous culture--beneficial *en masse*--the human future, indeed a highly interdependent world, will obey no prior temporal or spatial restrictions. An invigorated pursuit of risk become ritual, this paradigmatic transformation sounds the death knell for monolithic obstructionism; 1996 discoveries suggest that the genes seeking novelty engage during earliest development . . . a quite plausible explanation for the courageous curiosity evinced by children stimulated in utero.

Although the brain's global interactions are a rival measurement, it has been long if loosely conjectured in professional backrooms that our Paleolithic predecessors may have employed eight to ten percent of cortical potential, while at present we exhibit ten to twelve percent, with an additional two percent discriminating whatever defines genius.[3] Statistical quibbles or territorial claims aside, the developmental direction is decidedly toward rendering this resource more generous as the products of mind evolve in merit. But there remains one feature which distinguishes us among all local denizens, and because that fact epitomizes the empiricism necessary for so qualitative a claim it should emerge spotlit from the files of anatomical arcana: Certain neurons control rapidity of response, measurable efficiency, and this inhibitory function for complex organisms is physically far more prevalent in man than simians--by half again, over double that of less evolved mammals. Alwyn Scott, in *Stairway to the Mind,* graphically registers its telling effect: "The shorter this time becomes, the faster the shuttle can move about the enchanted loom"--also affording decelerative depth when elected.

---

[3] The traditional but now complementary instrument, IQ, identifies this hallowed ground with boundary stakes like 125, 145, 165 (perhaps influenced by which number approximates the score of its interpreter, ego's quantifiable bias); legitimate objections to a cognitive marker addressing creativity, social strengths, or empathic powers have introduced the emotional quotient.

Weaned from a sluggish media quotidian on snapshot television imagery--quicker pictures, shorter sound bites--today's youth may relax before music video's split-second montage, or casually master breathtaking computer games (like their pedestrian parents once pursued pinball as winning body linguists, with planned microchips storing and sending data at rates which require even faster operator interface) precisely because mental pace embracing expanded possibilities is responding to the selfsame technology mind has created for reduction in boredom. Notwithstanding this compressed tempo, the old neurogenetic ceiling--constructed before gestation's end--stubbornly impedes substantial grasp of content . . . producing diminished academic achievement everywhere while nonetheless accomplishing those considerable IQ gains recently observed in developed countries as the *Flynn effect* (but no paradox if students remain unmotivated by irrelevant curricula).[4]

However, our trend of enhanced reactivity (which Darwin observed in 1874 among challenged rabbits, and can be deduced from elevating electroencephalographic measurements of alpha rhythm along the evolutionary trail) bespeaks a yet more profound behavior breakthrough when, occasioned by prebirth enrichment, it lessens prejudice formed from slower and fewer cognitive outlets, perhaps damping prehistoric limbic system dominance due to increased neocortical linkages. Following fetal advantaging, an infant intensely attends televised cartoons or an older sibling's computer games as contemporary primers (their content less accessible than rapid morphology, the medium's earliest message; besides enjoying healthier physical nutrition, nascent mental appetite is now similarly measured in cyberbytes), signalling bandwidth liberation from the either/or thinking once required for survival, reduced time now

---

[4] Arguments against cultural or sensory sprinting can be at once attractive and eloquent (cf. *Slowness*, the short novel by Milan Kundera, also Mark Kingwell's May 1998 *Harper's* article, "Fast Forward: Our High-Speed Chase to Nowhere," which in passage scores the upcoming generation), yet invariably ignore that comparative context our primate ancestry represents, therefore speciational extent--the rigid strictures human retardation defines --because missing signposts on the path of shifting paradigms.

encouraging broader choices--not everyone need be predatory, and those who are may in the presence of unprecedented creative persuasion be charmed into compromise. An ancillary outcome worth the main attraction: Overcoming traditional impediments of race, sex, age, nationality, physical features, even language (software accomplishing what Esperanto could not), the memetic world linked more closely by each keyboard stroke between cultures should eliminate passports, currencies, and other defenses the reactionary self erects against its own quailing character; thoughts or feelings can finally stand free, no more clothed in superficialities we were long programmed to take for the person, an irresistible commonality revealed beneath.[5]

Summarizing the above, as neurology decrees so we succeed or succumb by comprehensive measures of attainment based upon capacity--organismic generally, human in specific. Developed under definitive trial and error according to niche limitations strictly shaping its passage, our consciousness so extensively recapitulating the cosmos in a few pounds of not terribly attractive tissue is an event never previously achieved by this planet's inhabitants--the primordial core wrapped with reptilian and mammalian layers to modern neocortical facility; yet facing massive demands born from our own powerful presence, desires, and ingenuity, those same transformative forces fostering the neotenous infancy of *Homo sapiens* have once again reached resolution through substantially extending brain growth. If it can be broadly claimed that culture is the overlaid function of biology, we are substituting with whirlwind velocity reciprocal altruism for avaricious genetics as a direct gain from increased neural capacitance. Like any organic feature facing incessant environmental change--the central cosmic dynamic--mind necessarily adapts or dies, human nature in tow; owing to causes both evolutionary and demographic, for continued existence of our kind and all remaining Earthly

---

[5] While the openness of computerized discourse appears for the present proportional to its anonymity, at least secondary exercises in mental or emotional freedom may through winnowing eventually produce primary and positive behaviors, if pervasive then an empathic gestalt.

41

residents (who make mortal presence possible), the new world order requires from us a proactive symbiosis, the closest cooperation between lifeforms: Empathy where it can arise must become innate . . . conscientious selection pressure exemplified.

Various elements permit this monumental metamorphosis, the first long known but only currently utilized to advantage. A century ago, the Spanish histologist, Nobel laureate Ramón y Cajal detected that neurogenesis experiences substantial curtailment of original production almost as soon as created, concurrent and then climactic; an explicative statement on the phenomenon came from Viktor Hamburger and Nobelist Rita Levi-Montalcini in 1949, supplemented by the work of J. Kerr *et al.* Generically--affecting vertebrates, spineless organisms, or even (as newly discovered) plants--preordained cell death at any time of life is termed *apoptosis*, with the earliest instance a genetic program for regular development, though one which must be triggered by external factors; in the human brain, coincident with full-term gestation's end, it amounts to a 50-75 percent reduction of neurons just manufactured, and some authorities quote numbers as high as 90 percent--leaving only a relatively small portion from the initial amount. While this attrition accompanies elaboration of the fetal protobrain (timeline **Figure I**), its final pruning under the orthodox hypothesis imparting a radically diminished lattice for subsequent growth, the net morphology--schematized by synthesizing several prominent if marginally divergent perspectives--may resemble the classic bell curve or Gaussian distribution depicted in **Figure II**, perhaps with a slightly plateaued apex. Cell dieoff complements the lifegiving enterprise, which seems odd, and is therefore deserving of explanation.

The cause for this curious process has been sought by mounting numbers of researchers, with Gerald Edelman's neuronal selectivity thesis most compelling:

> Whether [cell] death occurs spontaneously or not depends upon the establishment of connections in a projection field at an appropriate time, and this provides

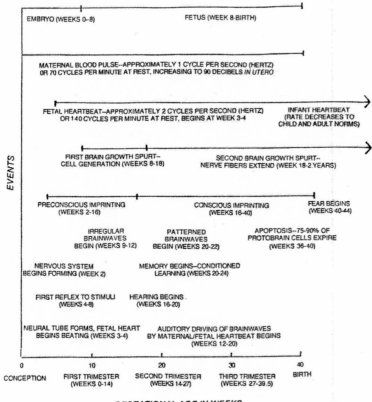

Figure 1

PROTOBRAIN CHRONOLOGY

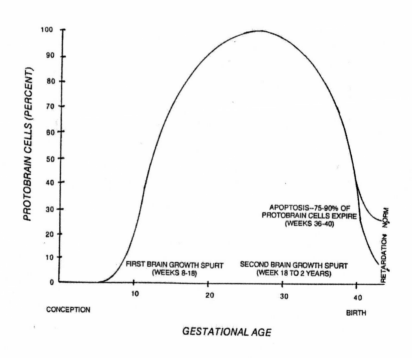

Figure II

PROTOBRAIN CELL DEATH

further evidence for selective and competitive models of neural patterning. No stronger case can be made for selection in neural patterning than that which derives from a consideration of the evidence on cell death. Up to 70 percent of cells die in certain areas during development, and the death can occur in a very short period of time. Most of this death is not preprogrammed but depends upon the neuron connecting to the appropriate innervation field. This must occur largely epigenetically and to some extent stochastically. . . . Thus, in two different individuals, while the same percentage of cells may die in a region, different cells die within each comparable population.

William Clark succinctly describes the engine evolutionary forces devised to drive organismic continuity, and how it is throttled for parsimonious functions within a setting; his *Sex and the Origins of Death* speaks of cellular demise at life's very outset, just after neurogenetic profligacy has commenced:

[Cells] act in response to a script embedded deep within them long ago, over which they have no control. Responding on cue to signals from their environment, they commit suicide.

The death of a cell by suicide is altogether different from necrotic cell death. Necrotic cell death is *cytocide*, the killing of a cell that does not want, and is not scheduled, to die. The cell dies in response to changes outside itself, some lethal alteration in its immediate surroundings . . . a cell dying of necrosis struggles violently, with everything at its disposal, to avoid death. The act of suicide by a cell is completely different. One cannot help being struck by how peaceful a death it seems, and all in all a rather unmessy one . . . .

The role played by cell suicide in the genesis of the nervous system represents an interesting and fundamental fact about the biology of this kind of dying in many cells: death is actually the default state for each of these neurons. From the moment a neuron is spun out of the central nervous system toward potential target cells, it is destined to die.

45

Only if it finds a connection with another cell will it be rescued from an otherwise certain death; it will receive chemical substances (called *growth factors*) from the target cell that in effect switch off the death program. In some respects this seems an incredibly wasteful way to build a nervous system. Each nerve cell that fails to make a connection with another cell in the body, and thus goes on to commit suicide, was very expensive to make in terms of biological energy. As with other tissue-shaping processes in which apoptosis plays a role, the development of the nervous system probably reflects a phylogenetically earlier process that was more efficient. Although now it may be considerably less efficient, overall it must be less expensive and more practical to use the inherited system at a lower efficiency than it would be to design a completely new way of building a nervous system from scratch. So the brain and the spinal cord build millions of cells they will never use, shunting the unselected into death through suicide.

Yet note that, according to Gerard Evan, "much of the detailed mechanism of cell death remains obscure"; in speaking about this definitive process for roundworms and humans:

> . . . of two cells arising by division of a mother cell, one would normally differentiate and the other die. If the second does not die, it develops in parallel with the first. The significance of these cells dying . . . is not entirely clear; individuals carrying mutant forms . . . grow to apparent maturity, but whether they reproduce normally and would survive in a competitive natural environment is not known. Probably not, since such individuals have not been observed in nature.

On the other hand, should that aberrant phenomenon produce a *favorable* organismic feature, presumably the asset would confer evolutionary prominence. But what controls this change, causality replicated again and again--a blueprint misread or circumstantial impingement? Does the genetic inheritance precisely predispose apoptosis for the protobrain of *Homo*

46

sapiens, opposing that which Clark notes to be an essential interaction with its environment? Evan furthers the issue, underscoring Edelman's explanation:

> In the nervous system, the nerve cells (neurons) proliferate during development and then establish contacts with each other by means of so-called synapses, thus generating a functional nervous system. Just as for the immune system, it is inherent in such a self-organizing structure that many cells fail to establish productive interactions and must be deleted. This might occur by some form of hierarchical supervisory mechanism constantly comparing the structure of the developing nervous system with a built-in plan, accompanied by the removal of supernumerary cells. The problem with such a concept is the immense complexity of the nervous system--a plan for its layout would be even more complex than the system itself. Where might such a plan be "kept" and how might it be implemented?

> It appears that programmed cell death is part of evolution's answer to self-assembly of the immune and nervous system. In the immune system, autoreactive lymphocytes encounter self-epitopes early in their differentiation within the primary lymphoid organs. This triggers their immediate suicide, with consequent deletion from the mature immune repertoire. Apart from some action by the proteases . . . the detailed mechanisms of both the triggers and the suicides themselves are unknown; a number of genes are clearly involved in the regulation of cell death but are probably not responsible for the death processes themselves.

> In the nervous system, neurons spontaneously commit suicide unless they are rescued by establishing productive connections with their neighbors. Superfluous, unconnected cells are self-deleting; no supervisor is needed to identify and kill them.

So, we see once more the powerful interplay of nature and nurture, most vital during neurogenesis when a rich ecological niche can reward innate appetite with information whose regard, interpretation, transmittal, storage, or retrieval through synaptic action cements lifetime advantage; like that salvational language from William Clark, Evan's description of possible resources being "rescued" by provident surroundings (random until culture accommodates) is serendipitous. If room for loss accompanies every gestation, our judicious intervention can increase the opposite odds; even mainstream researchers are downplaying genetic importance to emphasize the necessity of fetal enhancement, with Bernie Devlin *et al.* testing cognition's limits in a 1997 study comparing identical and fraternal twins against other siblings:

> . . . a new model may be required regarding the influence of genes and environment on cognitive function; and interventions aimed at improving the prenatal environment could lead to a significant increase in the population's IQ.

As Harvard paleontologist Stephen Jay Gould has reminded us without fail, despite its grandeur and accruing design, nature remains an inordinately crude progenitor, repeatedly recapitulating in miniature the Cambrian riot. To assure continuity of bloodlines, survival bias, during a season's spawn far more organisms than struggle through must be sacrificed-- plants, insects, fish. Take our own fecund origins: Illustrated in Chapter Two, for each fertilized ovum a plethora of perfectly qualified spermatozoa fall by the way, spurned suitors terminally wasting at the keep's closure . . . resoundingly slammed once an entrant is ensconced; runts slowed by stunted tails or faulty steering may be included among the rejectees--nonetheless playing programmed supportive roles--though most from the already screened one percent of healthy candidates would quite adequately meet the DNA mandate for procreation to transpire. Yet with what extravagance the germinal act happens! Emphasizing this teeming imbalance, genetic matchmakers striving for cultural elegance through reproductive design would recruit only one spermatic representative and the receptive egg-- a prototypically monogamous couple--forgetting how our fastidiousness is an assemblage of overcome mistakes stretching

48

back to the Big Bang; for biologic evolution arises not in the gentle eddies steadily giving birth to what typifies, but rather is struck wherever error or challenge meets opportunity, the microcosmic spume and roar of chance exploding without overt notice--covertly on schedule, chaos predictably constructing order, complexity's inevitable compasspoint.

Despite venerable reasons behind every pattern of conventional existence, variants have their own justification. As the fetal brain through almost cancerous overproduction is supplied with a larder of neural material, are we not merely witnessing prudent defensiveness against the inimical side of early life on Earth, protecting against predation--and a past for us so adjacent it still makes decisions in bedrooms, boardrooms, and war rooms? However, apoptosis illustrates an equally primal program which resists evolution--memorializing the moment, a particular time cloned; when that inertia attends consciousness, freezing potential, it incongrously constricts the mind's newfound freedom by defending a cellular hence behavioral plateau. In order to replicate genetic codes, the baseline requirement is sexual reproduction supported by organismic maintenance--protecting to maturity key components of species; for this bare minimum the brain's prolific first circuitry suffers an excision nearly as exuberant.

Nonetheless, humans have increasingly unshackled themselves from the rigid biologic dictum; for us a frontier never stays fixed. We choose by actively opposing passive inheritance to live longer and do more in our span than eat, breed, rear what results, or bristle at strangeness--over but a thousand generations rejecting the primordial order which dictated bestiality, territoriality, materiality--preferring sonatas and similies, laughter or love the ensignia of an exalted servitude. Not against but as siblings to less animate existence--prions, protozoa, periwinkles, primates--*Homo sapiens* is the most vigorously sensible statement in this vicinity: Lifting the genetic chorus, anthropically articulate, culture speaks for the cosmos . . . its native voice recently raised a garrulous octave.

Declaring reinforcement of the norm no longer the predominant goal existence seeks, the brain is fast becoming our

49

latest proving ground for behavioral innovation, decidedly during its fertile onset. Neurogenesis has become defined as the developmental period of maximum creativity; all subsequent intervention--familial, social, educational--*outside that to which potential can realistically respond* remains meaningless once the cerebral die is cast, an observation readily borne out *in extremis* when considering marked retardation. National constitutions may champion political equality among constituents unique as snowflakes or sandgrains, yet *with birth our basic faculties and capacities are too fully in place for much revision, irrespective of how life will flesh them out.* Existential choice, yes, but circumscribed by a cervical Charon: *Les jeux sont fait.*

It would be heartwarming if postnatal attempts at reversing incapacity held more than promise, however, exceptions to such failure are unfortunately just that. This is why fetal tissue raises substantial hope for slowing--perhaps reversing--mental decline at the senior end of life's spectrum (though new research with older stem cells, even postmortem, may also prove effective): transplanted vitality so potent its powers appear to counter aging's more noxious ravages, those which decelerate the corpus and its computer despite previous achievement . . . a grimly egalitarian reaper. But, should neural amplitude be introduced during pregnancy, this gift endures as part of mental architecture emerging past its initial experience with apoptosis, that terminal juncture (how ironic at birth!) when the brain is most lost[6] even while being gained.

---

[6] Recent reports about adult neuronal growth in monkeys, rats, and shrews --specifying the hippocampal learning and memory site--indicate merely token production contrasted with the fetal cascade, the same for 1998 detection (Peter Eriksson, Fred Gage, and colleagues at the Sahlgrenska University Hospital in Göteberg, and the Salk Institute for Biological Studies, La Jolla) of primitive human cells, and have yet to demonstrate durability or any functional interface among preexisting networks; should this discovery take place, its relatively minor percent of usage will serve restorative rather than developmental purposes. Some researchers believe these to be supporting glia instead of main neurons, while a Princeton University group led by Elizabeth Gould found that major stress or trauma limits such postnatal generation; evidence--from Jay Giedd and associates--

The distinct target, then, for alleviating stupendous troubles afflicting the world--with greater to come--resides in their influential origin: the now relatively defective mortal cortex, past a contextual prime, incapable of delivering that which newness solicits, as generically unstable as the history it inflicts upon everyone. What heretofore served mankind fittingly in the self-interest of parochialism--clinging to the moment lest lonely ego suffer outside infant skills--today seeks maturity with a famished appetite. And in the second millennium's waning this headlong quest trained technology upon the fruitful filagree of first thought, our neural network at inception. If selective pressure must urgently fashion streamlined or even totally original capabilities for us to face the otherwise insurmountable in a most fluid environment, among entities become autonomous through culture where else but out of group consent born individually could amplification arise--an occasion synonymous with the neurogenetic opening for optimization. Responding to desperation's demand for fundamental betterment by the only self-critical creature, biological defiance is dared: *Rescue the protobrain.* The alternative poses a precipitous devolution from effects of our own demographic superfluity; were the human future's foremost mission successful, its sturdier vessel would be equipped for venturing into an enormously enlarged ecology . . . a niche wide as the cosmos, perhaps (if multiverse theory holds) even broader.

That rationale inviting our conscious role in evolution appears with growing frequency; consider an example by Chiye Aoki and Phillip Siekevitz:

> . . . before the developing brain can attain the full power to process and analyze sensory experience, experience itself must place its own imprint on the finer structure of the brain . . . .
>
> How does experience mold the organization of the brain? . . . a sequence of molecular events, triggered by external stimuli . . . may contribute to plasticity . . . in the

---

of new corpus callosum connections in teenagers indicates cable growth, but not neurogenesis.

brain. Such molecular events may shape many of the mental features underlying our common humanity. By translating variations in early experience into variations in brain organization, they may also underlie some of our individual differences.

Indeed, natural antecedence points the way, as Peter Hepper believes:

Some low level experience may be essential for the newly-developed systems to function before coping with the greater intensity of sensations experienced after birth. Thus sensory experience may play an important role in the development of the individual's sensory neural structure. There can be little doubt that learning experiences early in the individual's life, especially during the formation of the neural system, may have a permanent effect on it. Experiential effects may increase neural growth, either by increasing arborization and/or connections within the system . . . . These experiential effects may increase the child's ability to learn and maintain information. Thus prenatal sensory and learning experiences may, by enhancing neural development, provide the foundation for future learning abilities. A role for experience in shaping the developing neural system allows the incorporation of greater flexibility and plasticity in the structure of the nervous system, which may in turn enable more adaptivity to the environment on the part of the individual.

To which one might add: ". . . thereby heightening survivability whenever more complex surroundings insist upon enhanced inhabitant responsiveness." Susan Ludington scrutinizes the matter further, her concluding sentence also made to me in a 1985 conversation when she learned of my research:

Fetuses' first synapses have been documented as early as the seventieth day after conception. Specialists in fetal and infant brain development stress that the fetal stimulation of a baby's senses can affect the development of these synapses.

In fact, the lack of these connections can cause nerve cells to die, especially in the eighth month of pregnancy. Current studies speculate that sensory stimulation of the fetus in utero during the last half of pregnancy (which, of course, creates more synapses) may act as a preventative to brain cell death . . . .

Through the miasma of ancient musings from many cultures, pointers toward ways for enhancing neurogenesis were first spied by the German physician Johann Spurzheim in 1815--surmising that nutritive blood flow to the brain could elaborate tissue--Italian anatomist Giacinto Malacarne, whose 1819 proposal paired environmental influence with cortical growth, and Ramón y Cajal, contributing a 1911 recommendation for mental work to proliferate neural connectivity . . . all prefiguring the stimulatory experiments of University of California at Berkeley neuroanatomist Marian Diamond; these are recounted in her 1988 book, *Enriching Heredity: The Impact of the Environment on the Anatomy of the Brain.* Just like a sinew experiencing exercise, the early mind's minute repositories of information stored as electrochemical quanta, joined by intricate conduits shunting relevant reports between finely spaced neurotransmitter interfaces, are fortified according to novel stimuli adequately repeated; if through redundant messages these sites, linkages, and intersections are maintained, *discernable* difference promotes growth--emphatically during the hyperplastic fetal period--securing for life those specially facilitated circuits should the patterned activity transpire before cortical dieoff completes full-term gestation, that watershed decimation which shapes more than any other the ultimate individual.

This, then, for subsequent generations becomes the most profitable ground science can presently till: *By some fortunate but not fortuitous effort, through our paramount developmental window, prebirth, let a mitigating means salvage from the protobrain whatever portion of outdated genetic inheritance can afford less fettered talent; grow the now requisite neurology.* That perforce hubristic enterprise depends upon a few crucial

53

mechanisms indigenous to the womb--those long known yet interpreted here in the light of new findings, others so immediate their importance is just being felt.

Chapter Six--*Beyond the Primal Imprint*

I hear it in the deep heart's core.

William Butler Yeats,
"The Lake Isle of Innisfree," 1893

Because an individual's most durable distinction may derive from how information is acquired during a growth stage before learning ever had been thought possible, it was not surprising that pieces of the prenatal puzzle lay unassembled when I came upon them two decades ago. Even so, partial precedent tantalized neuroscience for years--notably surrounding apoptosis in the fetal brain; for instance, there is a 1978 enticement by Charlotte Mistretta and Robert Bradley:

> During neural development the processes of cell division, migration, growth, differentiation, and death all take place. Depending on when the organism is exposed to a particular modification of its usual sensory experience, any one of these ongoing processes could be affected. It has often been suggested that one of the least complex ways to modify the developing nervous system would be through the process of cell death . . . .
>
> It is odd that the possibility of prenatally modifying mammalian brain and behavioral development through intrauterine sensory stimulation has received so little attention . . . . Perhaps in the future we will be able to learn more about the relative effectiveness of the intra- versus extrauterine environments in influencing the developing nervous system in different species . . . .
>
> But this new understanding will probably come more quickly if investigators working in sensory systems other than vision use more varied approaches in manipulating early sensory experience and in analyzing subsequent effects.

55

Perhaps the chief obstacle to professionals appreciating the fetus as student is the outdated assumption that our first domicile describes an exclusively medical domain. While fewer physicians treat pregnancy like a disease--this pathology of younger women but incidentally producing babies--most obstetricians are open to evidence of infant acumen within the vestibule tattered textbooks claim more vacuous than instructive; nonetheless, this practitioner knowledge frequently extends to third trimester capability alone. And yet as diligent researchers now realize, no sooner has conception transpired then schooling fully enrolls the embryo.

Since environmental features are defensively monitored from the absolute start of life by an elementary chemical system already deciphering data to organismic utility, the evolving nervous system enhances but does not alter that distinct manner in which prenatal understanding takes place. Although employed by behaviorists to suggest an early influence or simply a patterned and much repeated stimulus with which the recipient remains bonded the rest of its life, technically--as Eckhard Hess specifies--*imprinting* embraces only that period before fear commences . . . in humans the latter occurs shortly after birth; this distinctive provision for first information-processing antedates the advent of will, constituting indispensable neurogenetic nutrition prior to development's definitive window closing. Because lack of experience has not yet accrued enough memory to evoke pain's premonition, consciousness relates to negative events differently preceding a qualitative threshold being crossed--and that parallels parturition. An infant's cry upon entering the ex utero world is decidedly other than a similar expression but days later; we register what hurts, yet not from anxiety. . . cringing anticipation comes later.[1]

---

[1] Seasoned veterinarians realize that a newborn creature repeatedly stroked over its entire body by the caregiver will never again resist that touch, therefore making later assistance much easier, how physical and emotional proximity welds together the imprinted sensorium; this is why, unless a medical emergency intervenes, the shortest distance between an alienated

Therefore, a quite particular perception describes our opening months as inhabitants of life's premier classroom, warm and maternally chaperoned in utero though they may be; how we record treat or trauma is diametrically unlike what follows. Before, choice is not involved--the fetal system locks unto whatever is structurally simplistic and redundant, actuarial biochemistry supporting neural bookkeeping keen but to the relevant--whereas afterward the mind gains gradual independence from that genetic program which rang the initial schoolbell. While the subliminal portion of this rudimentary influence most interested me--as *preconscious imprinting*--Lee Salk contributes an explanation which includes the overtly attentive part:

> Imprinting compels the organism to seek continued sensory stimulation by coming into contact with its environment and by so doing enhances the development of behaviour patterns that have adaptive value, through associative learning.

So eager is the crude computer for germane data, it will fixate upon any stimulus matching the morphological template, a formationist matrix composed of archetypal outlines such as D'Arcy Thompson described: *contrast, movement, size, shape, duration,* and the like, with these refined as mastery mounts. Fit or flawed, cornerstones of being this monolithic will not shift; they are emplaced until the organism expires, those selfsame coordinates that programmed visual receptors for rapid horizontal scanning once our arboreal exodus to the savannas took place, then epic nomadism--predation's early warning system. Gerald Edelman draws a number of astute conclusions:

> . . . animals initiate true learning only when an element of novelty, surprise, or violation of expectation is present; the first occurrence of such a surprise in real time is critical
> . . . .

---

or loving life is straight form birth canal to mother's breast--imperative tactile, visual, gustatory, and olfactory contact, ideally protracted.

If an animal is to learn or match its brain states (involving synaptic efficacies, motor responses, etc.) to signals representing relationships between objects and events and then develop adaptive behavior, how can it recognize these objects and events? Clearly, the answer involves perceptual categorization, the neural basis of which must already exist in the animal . . . this basis is neuronal group structure and selection and in the satisfaction of continuity requirements by appropriate global mapping and reentry.

The ability to learn thus requires that these means for perceptual categorization first be in place. Perceptual categorzation in itself is clearly not sufficient, however, to fulfill adaptive needs in either evolutionary or somatic time.... Some *conventional* adaptive means must be at hand to deal with the sampling of such events according to contingency, to their juxtaposition in time, and to their assumed relation to cause. This means is learning.

The main point to be made . . . is that neuronal group selection could not occur *adaptively* without behavior that can deal with such event contingencies. This is so both because neuronal group selection cannot occur without variance in behavior (inasmuch as it depends upon variation in brain states) and because, in a varying environment, adaptation requires learning. In other words, it is learning that makes categorization adaptive. This is not a circular argument--the apparatus capable of perceptual categorization must be built by evolutionary means into the structure of the brain and nervous system *before* the events of learning ever take place. The basic embryological facts...support such a view: development of a primary repertoire does not require any behavior of the kind that occurs in postnatal life....

Responsible science begins with careful and exhaustive investigation, in the uterine domain aided beyond precedent by technology during the last decades. When fiber optics facilitated television's entry to the womb, it succeeded sonic observations which had revealed truths revising millennial guesswork. More than any other finding about human origins except protobrain cell death, what was heard inside the abdomens of pregnant mothers provoked incredulity among fetologists (still astonishing to many physicians), with developmental psychology even further intrigued. For if an omipresent imprint serves to construct the permanent binary, polarized, dichotomous framework housing our lives, then resounding from placental walls came the trumpet of Armageddon in reverse time.

By inserting a miniature, liquid-impervious microphone through the dilating cervix of a woman pending labor, injurious neither to her nor the unborn occupant, Japanese obstetrician Hajime Murooka conducted in the early 1970s an experiment whose outcome reverberated seismically.[2] This voyage by hydrophone--into the amphitheater we inhabit when every fundamental human aspect experiences creation--came upon a completely unanticipated soundscape; in one acoustic probe of our earliest environment an edifice of incorrect assumptions collapsed. For untold centuries there came from eminent philosophers and scientists, lacking the technological means of determination, understandably wrongheaded speculation about the inside sonic terrain, but few before Murooka had conducted a replicable test.

This recorded truth stood in utter contrast to the traditional view that infancy receives natural protection in utero from the noisy outer world; opposing the romanticized notion of inner tranquility and buffered repose, a simple listening device revealed an explosive universe ricocheting with percussions louder than thunder--causing lifetime effects. The fetus was being bombarded by incessant detonations . . . nary a quiet corner, asleep or awake demonstrably no place to hide. Unlike prevalent retreats from adult responsibility, the modern mind had not deliberately avoided this reality, rather it first lacked the proper tool and then evidence before an investigation indirectly urged by one exasperated conductor with the Tokyo Symphony

---

[2] As it has been for many discoveries where timelines seem dependably contingent (witness Darwin's competitively energized agenda), the question of priority prevails here; if Murooka was not first then others--R. J. Bench in 1968 or W. R. Henshall, 1972--were approximately contiguous, so my subsequent remarks still apply.

(a serendipitous friend of Murooka) remonstrating that too many young music students appeared tone deaf--so how early could this appreciation begin? The result of circumspect inquiry dispelled a reigning paradigm as surely as Copernicus replaced Ptolemy's geocentric cosmos, requiring the relevant parameters to be thoroughly reexamined.

From psychological vantage, it would be nice to believe differently--that character falls from a prenatal grace which salvational therapy could restore--but engineering's inner ear insists the matter is just not so. The womb's natural cacaphony derives from various sources which can be noted in order of increasing importance. Beginning outside, whatever registers with the mother--any sound in her surroundings except that below the level of a raised whisper--reaches the unborn infant; planes overhead, street life, television, radio, room conversation . . . almost all nearby sonic phenomena visit the covert listener. Some diminution and muffling occur--an attenuation of about 30 decibels due to abdominal tissue, fluid, and bone barriers (comparatively constant for thin or heavy women)--but like hearing underwater or through a glass held to an irresistible hotel wall, discernment is remarkable; were translation no problem, few secrets could be kept from the fetus.

Even more fascinating, the interior itself exemplifies an incredibly audible source: stomach rumblings, bowel activity, the maternal voice (which becomes clearer if a mother leans forward and speaks at slightly increased volume). But way beyond these busy activities, the foremost sonic feature booms inescapably; omnipresent as the amniotic sea roars an urgent, surflike crescendo of blood racing by the placenta, with a mean sound level for its lower frequencies at 80 decibels, cresting to 95 (prior to this 1996 figure, by K. S. Gerhardt and R. M. Abrams, less loud readings obtained)--much like a freight train or rock music band at arm's length. This persistent hammering, stronger depending on fetal location yet not absent for an instant, surges with a speed governed by its generator, the mother's heart; when she exerts herself, the rate races, while as sleep transpires cardiation slows to the signature frequency.

No adult who hears a recording of those truly native drumbeats can avoid being overwhelmed: Throughout life's basement resounds the seminal symphony, that music so important to human inception and each experience thereafter, whether apart from or manufactured by the mind; before this sirenic presence it is impossible if not to dance then at minimum we sense an energy affecting pulse, fingers, and feet, the body synchronized with what feels like the quintessential cosmic flow. In stark summary, gestation may resemble a howling chaos from which birth could seem an utter relief--despite every delivery room's multisensory drama.

One might imagine such extreme volume must obstruct any competition, yet the glaring question of how, bathed in blare, a fetus can discriminate ex utero sonic stimuli is answered by an odd though natural phenomenon called stochastic resonance, where the womb's tumult actually augments what it would appear to block--see "The Benefits of Background Noise," by Frank Moss and Kurt Wiesenfeld. Despite barriers of flesh and sound, the sensible message gets through.

But the main lesson from Murooka's finding could not be denied: Every dimension of this phenomenal activity matched the rigid requirements for imprinting--simplicity, recurrence, and exposure prior to fear's onset--which Lee Salk had determined during the 1960s. Although only inferring an in utero aortic sound level impressive to the fetus, his postnatal observations were fully borne out by the later technological tapping of their antecedent source. In vivid proof, Salk reported that the human heartbeat pattern--*with no close contender*--substantially calms newborns, provides them a generous weight gain, influences the way adults hold infants, and establishes the rhythm for most music. While a few researchers surmised the low frequency of these maternal bloodpulses might not register with the fetus (presumably questioning how soon audition is possible while slighting that first sensory universe which, like the visceral system, quite richly addresses our earliest neural receptors in synesthetic display, one vehicle instructing the others as they become functional), Salk's observations--in addition to

61

numerous later experiments--confirmed precisely the opposite: Evidence of imprinting was definitive.

The ironclad case could be made for an event of maximum magnitude continuously being engraved as life's blueprint, the hardest wiring, a stamp whose repercussions on vertebrates would follow to their final days. The importance of this primary environmental edict is stated by James Grier Miller: "Associations established early in the life of a system are more permanent than those established later." Perhaps why sound represents so influential a stimulus is that the other young senses besides hearing--like taste or touch--are less exposed to patterns of frequent redundancy, and the pathway for maximum input, sight, only opens late in term with little occasion for use save apprehending diffuse light from a bright source, hematically filtered pink through the abdominal wall.

The paradigmatic uterine omnipresence of maternal blood rhythm cannot help but invite science to its natural task of inquiry, pursuing wherever direction leads; as Mac Freeman implores: ". . . we surely ought to explore the beckoning possibility that our mother's heart was the first drum to which we learned to dance." Fred J. Schwartz's analysis gives a rationale:

> The synaptic network in the fetal brain as well as infant brain undergoes learning dependent reorganization. This process involves synaptic pruning, the regression of neural circuits as well as the synaptic sprouting of the developing brain . . . . Since fetal hearing is probably the major component of this learning dependent synaptic pruning and sprouting, the fetus is participating in a second and third trimester auditory amphitheater that is perhaps more important than any other classroom. It is apparent that we have only begun to explore the connection between sound and neurobiological development in the fetus . . . .

Is this why, speaking about fetal cardiation's seemingly premature onset, Myron Hofer points out (in *The Roots of Human Behavior*):

62

. . . there remains a major mystery in prenatal life--the question of why sensory and motor functions develop and exhibit activity, weeks and even months before they have any clear usefulness to the baby. We find it hard to accept that there is all this function without some purpose.

At minimum, heartbeat becomes our performance baseline, arguably shaping neurogenesis to outmoded survival requirements restricted through apoptosis. The sway of this energetic--but no longer enterprising--governor is so supreme we exit the birth canal under a neotenous tutelage preparing us for predators . . . and not much more; atop that numbing mandate rests every mortal failing or achievement to date.

It might be said that from the moment a first note is struck, each increment of order follows--as true for embryogenesis as cosmogenesis, personal and pervasive Big Bangs (deferred witness thanks to astronomy's better eyes, though no less valid than visibly contemporaneous). Without exaggeration, whether with individuals or a species, humanity--indeed, life's complete cohort--owes the totality of being to what enters consciousness, despite the extent, at its primal point; this existential nexus is hardly new: *Nihil in intellectu, quod non ante in sensu,* a sensory mind--no matter what illusion--never the reverse. Thought, imagination, and dream originate other than where they are performed; even the most serious preSocratic playfulness aside, we interpret, not invent the universe--redesign remains a secondary process.

Apart from the classic observational question concerning uncertainty (and as axiomatic as it may appear unless entirely unanticipated laws apply), once an initial action takes place time commences: This original instance sets the criterion with which everything after can be compared--and why nothing is repeated since its recurrence by definition becomes uniquely subsequent. Therefore, an unprecedented phenomenon of sensory significance simultaneously bifurcates reality into the prototypic singularity and all except it, not dualistic tonal or spatial *otherness* alone but adding a temporal measure which

63

thenceforth demarcates the two. And from this elemental diversity springs the only dimensions neural and cultural consciousness can know. That binary codex sets forth in strictest terms the behavioral bible most earthly creatures obey, chiefly us: Humankind marches smartly to the heart's unceasing cadence, not just because it regulates blood flow but is incidentally civilizing our corner of the cosmos by alerting earliest mind to the most overarching archetype whence succeeding form achieves meaning, be it number, name, or image.

The American poet, Robert Hass, has probed the rudimentary aspects of rhythm in "Listening and Making," a chapter from his bountiful *Twentieth Century Pleasures*; several excerpts lend emphasis here:

> . . . we are pattern-discerning animals, for whatever reason in our evolutionary history. We attend to a rhythm almost instinctively, listen to it for a while, and, if we decide it has no special significance for us, we can let it go; or put it away, not hearing it again unless it alters, signalling to us--as it would to a hunting or grazing animal--that something in the environment is changed. This process is going on in us all the time, one way or another. It is the first stage, wakeful, animal, alert, of the experience of rhythm . . . it calls us to an intense, attentive consciousness.

> Repetition makes us feel secure and variation makes us feel free. What these experiences must touch in us is the rhythm of our own individuation.

> Rhythmic repetition initiates a sense of order. The feeling of magic comes from the way it puts us in touch with the promise of a deep sympathetic power in things: heartbeat . . . .

Although being steered to these lines many years after my conceptualization of fetal awareness at both its covert and conscious levels, I was quite moved by this eloquent

64

reinforcement--an appreciation beyond the cognitive. From interpersonal perspective Peter Hepper has touched upon this necessary complement where it begins:

> Intrauterine auditory experience appears to convey rhythmic information to the fetus, and numerous studies have demonstrated the ease with which rhythmic auditory stimuli are learned by the fetus. Social interactions after birth require turn-taking, based upon rhythmicity. For example, a conversation requires one person to talk, the other to listen, and then the roles are reversed. Rhythm, which is important for later social interactions, may be initially experienced in the womb . . . . Prenatal learning may be important for the development of attachment and for social development of the individual.

Mentation's counterpart--the infinite expanse of mood--emoting barbarity or bliss, equally proceeds from a neural reservoir we are finding had better be full so the affable offspring might counsel its intemperate ancestor, with no limit to overflow.

Faced with observations like these, I therefore kept returning to a question which new discoveries made even more poignant: Since compounding research also documents that substantial gains in reasoning skills, from spatial pattern-recognition to puzzle-solving, are the direct product of enhanced musical exposure and training in preschool children, *what would happen if neurogenesis started to witness subtle yet sequential changes in its usual diet of information, new syllables incrementally enunciated in the mother tongue?* Receptive but to imprints, might the fetal memory bank then substantially enlarge, supply lines of deathless data increase in number and speed, assimilation time decrease--precisely those features later learning facilitates? Because the prenatal brain has been genetically cued to scour its environment in quest of primordial sense--a search for terrestrial intelligence--the structure and content afforded by maternal heartbeat (along with that faster relative within the same corpus), why not draw upon natural example? Could neuronal connections be made before birth which would never link normally--our dated biologic heritage--then encouraged through repeated use to remain, potentially countering apoptosis as a permanent behavioral edge . . . the opposite of retardation's tragic toll? As Jerome H. Barkow, Leda Cosmides, and John Tooby note:

> . . . "learning" is turning out to be a diverse set of processes caused by a series of incredibly intricate, functionally organized cognitive adaptations, implemented in neurobiological machinery. . . .

The "good trick" (Daniel Dennett identifying how fitness landscapes fortuitously elevate) was to capitalize upon what Wallace Stevens saw behind artful motives--enjoying a pleasurable interlude, then moved further by that force driving consciousness toward its more convoluted niche, stasis and its displacement similarly explained: "Oh! Blessed rage for order . . . ."

Just as nature's growth sequence takes place in cumulative fashion subject to environmental interface, epigenetically, the stairstep pace of accruing knowledge we call *curricular* shapes our entire knowledge process: Two doubled becomes four only after the mind understands a single integer's addition to itself; similarly, quantum physics derives from calculus through an ascending complexity. In terms of scholastic possibility at the prenatal stage, this principle especially applies: Despite the aforementioned anomaly of newborn chicks cowering at a hawk's silhouette--their genetic imprint for survival--human recognition registers from experience alone, engaged or imagined; strictly speaking, *our neural past is the only prologue we can know.* Though unavoidably prejudiced by adult perception, plausibility loomed: *Could an exclusively fetal vocabulary be constructed? Beyond that traditionally endowed, would a compounding code signal germinative ground rules to the unborn child?* And what conceivably might constitute building blocks for our most rudimentary grammar, the wordless world from which civilization's innate garrulity--text in all its marvelous or tedious guises--must derive?

So, the cortical clash was engaged beyond drawing board strategems: Previous to the protobrain nearly expiring as full-term birth transpires, erect upon its cultural subflooring--the heart's heavily etched tones and tempo, that language every prenate has increasingly followed from conception--syntactic progressions; then repeat these frequently enough for durable enhancement of mental structure. By this practice we would be establishing richer cognitive and behavioral resources, consequently lifetime potential, than the previous mortal plateau . . . predetermining higher functionality. If redundant patterns reassure even while risking disinterest, they reduce fear of the unknown and serve as our starting point for relevant departures-- enough alike to be identified yet sufficiently different for interest pursuing as capability affords: However haunting or underlaid, unless perseverated pathologically no single melody constitutes a human's musical repertoire; and should that extended sonic range predate massive cell death at gestation's full-term end, the subsequent brain could lastingly benefit. Such was the proposition I put forward in 1982, under the general concept termed *prelearning* (used differently in other contexts).

But a worthwhile notion cannot thrive in the abstract; Gerald Edelman's caveat for this or any ideational trial exorcised physical inaction:

> A theory is valuable only insofar as it proposes detailed and particular mechanisms to explain a wide variety of phenomena in its domain and insofar as it stimulates new experiments.

If a thought has virtue, its pragmatic point ultimately arrives-- without testing, mere speculation remains; Gayle Ormiston and Raphael Sassower in an intriguing treatise, *Narrative Experiments: The Discursive Authority of Science and Technology*, rouse a hound named engineering, the course desperate parents recommend to indolent adolescents whose daydreams too closely recall their own: ". . . ideas make sense only when they are placed into action." Allen Wheelis envisions no detour from the sole vivacious avenue in town, waving bravery on with a tattered but accurate roadmap: ". . . the way to live is to act." So doing, dream and deed merge, imagination infusing work for that integrity which constitutes our one valid existence.

Given the stakes of growing personal and group failure across all peer output or behavior categories, my musings assumed a burden procrastination would no longer bear; remaining idle in the face of this propitious possibilty became an ethical indictment. At last that tremulous time had come to access the creature in question, extending Spengler's maxim: "Life has purpose--the fulfillment of what was established at one's birth."

Chapter Seven--*A Cardiac Curriculum*

This is the story of how we begin to remember
This is the powerful pulsing of love in the vein
After the dream of falling and calling your name out
These are the roots of rhythm
And the roots of rhythm remain

Paul Simon, "Under African Skies," 1986

Once uterine music was captured by acoustic science, an awestruck outside world began directing it back to the fetus. Hajime Murooka commercialized his discovery as a bestselling 1974 phonograph disk labeled *Lullaby from the Womb*, containing the maternal auditorium's sounds alone, then classical melodies recorded over them; entranced audiences found the refrain hauntingly familiar--since everyone had imprinted to its archetypal cadence--with pregnant mothers intuitively pressing their abdomens against loudspeakers replaced a few years later by headphones from the Sony Corporation's new audiocassette player. All the same, in Murooka's theme song being routed to unborn children, were they hearing anything not essentially native? Apart from compositions available as well on other recordings, certainly one more cardiac resource resounded throughout the placental cavity, yet that pattern was structurally identical with its original source except for damping by interposed flesh and fluid. Still, the Rosetta stone of incipient linguistics had been precisely located, key to our sonic baseline, and sufficient to formulate a fetal lexicon . . . though enterprising parents radically departed from that natural text.

When my late wife, Helga Bothe, chanced upon a 1982 radio report of one Japanese-American family who had prenatally exposed four daughters to an eclectic education--the alphabet, mathematics, children's tunes and stories--she proposed standardizing the practice. An instant response was inexplicably distinct to me--see how inspiration can arrive in Laura Day's

Practical Intuition--therefore I assessed as feasible what seemed the appropriate technology while at first but slightly less vague than my spouse about its sonoral content (searching for Karl Popper's "unusual combination of stimuli"). Nonetheless, this research across a wide span of disciplines soon developed the hypothesis which, once shaped into theory, could support an initial trial for that distaff suggestion; multiple miscarriages dissuaded our own validation, so we would have to find a suitable volunteer.

Consolidated, the rationale for application embraced a causal chain: Studies under reputable investigators showed the vertebrate fetus more responsive to sound than a stimulus from any of the other senses, with in utero maternal heartbeat imprinted as an informational foundation for the developing brain--its earliest circuitry programmed to expire at full-term birth--and learning among all known species advanced through incremental levels of complexity . . . assimilating unknowns as they were referenced by relevant memory. Most importantly, however, there was ample evidence--for neurology whose structure from a laboratory perspective resembled ours--that fetal education initiated physical and behavioral changes of deepest significance.

For many decades Marian Diamond had been verifying that multimodal stimulation of Norway rats during gestation produced a vast furtherance in efficiency for the postnatal pups when they negotiated obstacle courses, and--from tissue analysis--their mental apparatus responsible was notably different. As reprised in her book, *Enriching Heredity*, the glial or helper cells composing these abler brains, also key cortical areas--facilitated preceding fetal apoptosis--became substantially more developed, revealing sophistication much like that of a mammal farther up the evolutionary rungs. Since patterns are appreciated neurogenetically by whatever avenues can adequately convey stimuli, a synesthestic mix registering cognitive transients and traditions, Diamond's various trials suggested equivalent sonic value from other sensory influence; the increased corpus callosum findings--among musicians trained just after infancy--of Gottfried Schlaug (referenced before in connection with Donald Shetler's project) bear keen comparison because he believes early exposure to rhythm proliferates and better insulates neural linkages, thereby speeding motor connections which bridge the brain's hemispheres.

And this evidence correlated excitingly with the cortical morphology of a human considered by professionals and public alike to epitomize superlative scientific as well as humanitarian achievement--Albert Einstein. When Diamond's research team examined selected tissue from his long-preserved brain, cellular presence was found noticeably richer . . . an implicative parallel to what her rat work had revealed. Neurologically speaking, complexity of material structure corresponds with mentation creating manifold products, outcome directly linked to input, scope derived from how early and amply succor takes place.

One enigmatic interjection is worth elaborating: Despite no extraordinary genetic endowment, was Einstein the unwitting recipient of a prenatal sonic legacy, perhaps music regularly practiced by his expectant mother since it has been diversely documented that she taught him and his sister the piano while both were quite young? Would esthetic dedication have meant that her station at the family instrument's sonorous keyboard never ceased--frequently playing duets with employees from the firm where her husband worked--next to which a captive but quite possibly captivated learner listened . . . whose newborn head size was extreme?[1] All records imply this rich gestational history. We know she encouraged his early and lifelong affiliation with the violin, yet did maternal suggestion extend to the pattern-appreciative origin of a life that would eventually help explain the cosmic order itself? Like Conan Doyle's cerebrally gifted fictive sleuth, Einstein's confessed sole emotional outlet was music, at which--recalling Donald Shetler's results--he showed youthful promise; recent findings for substantial cognitive gains from childhood exposure to rhythm

---

[1] These features of egoistic interest congruent with my own generous cranial dimensions before birth and since; as the prenatal psychologists sagely recommend: *For a subject's prime coordinates, ask their mother about every detail of her pregnancy.*

assume special importance here. Still, though quite intelligent, why was his sister not also exceptional--had change in maternal circumstance deprived her of similar prebirth stimulation?

Moreover, may we unfashionably venture some Lamarckian, even macroevolutionary mechanism (centerpiece of my kindred volume)--recoding a key genetic instruction for the fetus if substantially mitigated apoptosis conferring survival benefits transpires in utero? How skilled were Einstein's children? Apart from the daughter whose existence after infant adoption is questionable (Michele Zackheim recently probed this mystery), one son became an accomplished hydraulics engineer with pronounced musical tastes, the other was precocious in literature and the arts, exhibiting astute psychological insight alongside schizophrenia; accompanying his father on violin and piano-- their only shared moments--further demonstrates giftedness in a family whose emotional description defines dysfunctionality.

Could, as current biographies aver (see the contribution of Dennis Overbye), Einstein's tarnished brilliance--scientifically superior though socially deficient--have been compensatory in the way autistic savants evince (perhaps the source for intelligent but aloof normalcy), because his prenatal music exposure established neurogenetic bias that was still inadequate to cross a cortical threshold for comprehensive gains since the sonic enrichment, despite incremental patterns, remained uncurricularized? Was that the fragmented inheritance left to his bright if flawed offspring? Might the humanism he exemplified throughout later life be atonement at realizing fault lines running deep . . . even to the shared--possibly borrowed, Einstein referencing in a lately discovered letter "our" work--origin of relativity theory with his first wife, she whose considerable talents either atrophied or went unreported by an ambitious husband, her subsequent fate unknown? Since this new scholarship is revealing rather substantial character flaws in the embroidered private legend, perhaps motivation for expiatory public acts, could his 1918 address to the Physical Society be interpreted on two levels (whether its surface meaning characterizes everyone's artifice)?

Man tries to make for himself in the fashion that suits him best a simplified and intelligible picture of the world; he then tries to some extent to substitute this cosmos of his for the world of experience, and thus to overcome it. This is what the painter, the poet, the speculative philosopher, and the natural scientist do, each in his own fashion. Each makes this cosmos and its construction the pivot of his emotional life . . . to find . . . the peace and security which he cannot find in the narrow whirlpool of personal experience.

As with Darwin's revisionist history, sooner or later haloes lose luster (save those indelibly glistered during gestation). In any case, be the phenomenally endowed a Buddha, Confucius, Christ, Michelangelo, Kepler, Mozart, or Hawking, this remains fertile ground for fetal detectives and doctoral candidates to investigate--an archeology of formative greatness.

Yet apart from any charismatic assessment of prodigiousness, clinical experiments commanded unequivocal attention: Meticulous science by Marian Diamond had located site and explanation for unprecedented facility in a cerebral system more kin than not to ours, with lucid clues that *Homo sapiens* could be also optimized . . . tenably, as just hinted, should the advantage endure--perhaps triggering an exponential expansion--among subsequent generations.

Upon comprehending a supremely implicative challenge, I sought coherence by devising an equation of empirical format though amorphous substance. Potential for an organism, however this capacity is defined--the entity's total worth expressed in physical, mental, or other productive quanta, ideally combined--could be assessed at longitudinal cross sections through a metaphoric formula (each element ephemeral, apart from "Time's wingèd chariot hurrying near"), the object being to explore relationships between variables and see whether fruitful inferences might arise:

$$P_o = \frac{G \quad E}{A}$$

73

If nature expressed as genetic (G) inheritance--cladistic morphology imbued in the new life owing to an interpretive bloodline--is modified from environmental (E) input or its lack, and the interplay between these factors determined momentarily by the creature's age (A), at least symbolic value would follow. While this *law of ontogenetic potential* might produce a heirarchy less numerical than numinous, it did articulate why early outweighs later stimulation: When the denominator grows large, a senior of any species must wrestle an amassing gravity from assets fixed in their DNA birthright--yet can call only upon resources mediated with diminishing senses; sadly, in later years the odds decline for a personal future as full as previous experience, and waning memory is pitiable compensation. The meaning was too evident: Apart from that which advanced consciousness on Earth has undertaken by creative archiving and computation to multiply skills at any age, mental ravages over time may be deferred through expanding the initial faculty-- *whoever starts with more neurology so ends.*

What makes this deceptively facile solution possible yields upon further analysis of the above exercise. Since the genetic program does not vary from its emplacement at conception (except with bioengineering or retrograde changes postulated in my collateral book), and accreting moments reduce remaining opportunity, the sole locus left to beneficially intervene must be the environment--for optimal effect when life has barely begun, as explicated by a *law of neurogenetic potential*:

$$P_n = D \ I$$
$$D = f \ I$$

Here the decisive determinant is apoptosis, in this instance fetal brain cell death (D) concluding full-term gestation, its typical extent lessened through imprintable (I) stimuli--the former as much a function of the latter as the reverse--whereby across the organism's life stage an ameliorated and replicable measure

74

performs . . . choreographed consistently until the next environmental shift elicits evolutionary response.

With the dynamic for change described, deployment beckoned. As previously noted, if substance sprung from idea is the pediment to respectable scientific endeavor, practice assumes the superior portion because proof cannot stop with its proposal. And since handiwork must follow the head's instructions (however heartening or viscerally sensed), so I needed to translate a map of the beginning mortal brain into language infancy anywhere could understand--well before this activity had been traditionally acknowledged. That next stage commenced with a schematic depicting human protogrammar, then implemented through an extension of the sonic arts.

Unlike decipherment--where knowledge flows backward in time, originating from clues--creating a lingua franca for the fetus meant the opposite of this process: What other starting point than that which first acts upon the womb's sounding board, our monotonally inscribed DNA slate, lucidly identified by hydrophone. In *Consciousness Explained*, under an apropos rubric--"The Birth of Boundaries and Reasons"--Daniel Dennett characterizes cosmogenesis; if applied to environmental influence during neurogenesis, how pertinent (inverting its value, zero paradoxically becomes an ultimate sum--perhaps initiated by the *Casimir effect*, a human universe replete with cognizance and all seriatim thoughts):

> In the beginning, there were no reasons; there were only causes. Nothing had a purpose, nothing had so much as a function; there was no teleology in the world at all. The explanation for this is simple: There was nothing that had interests.

Philosophy and poetry often speak one tongue (these days the conversation increasingly includes science); in reference to our prototypic linguistic instance their reports coincide, specific as a noun's article, with Wallace Stevens rhetorically questioning, "Where was it one first heard of the truth: the the." While hindsight may view this reductionist approach as too evident, at first appearance every postnatal supposition had to be

75

silenced; why parents assumed their in utero audience would welcome Brahms or Bible verses was because bias is indubitably blind to source--how could a genetic clone not share procreant taste (a presumption adolescence invariably battles)? But by tackling the problem as our prescholastic mindset, fidelity to the unborn child's real surroundings would be preserved; if science is not ultrasensitive it errs, and in this instance the unequivocal zerobase insisted upon abandoning each prejudice . . . truth's requisite rite of purification.

Fortunately, new technology allowed that exact effort: hardware invented by sonic artisans Raymond Kurzweil--now engineering artificial intelligence--and Stevie Wonder, then employed by fellow creators like the Grateful Dead band's drummer, Mickey Hart (whose later perinatal recording, *Music To Be Born By*, builds on the cardiac imprint), or the incomparably eclectic composer, Paul Simon. Electronics had been moving musicians much beyond sound amplifiers and hybrid instrumentation, with synthesizers introducing an exciting range to the acoustic repertoire. Of these sensory extensions-- what word processors did for verbal text--perhaps their epitome is the digital sampling device, which could convert any acoustic event to electrical impulses in binary code. This versatile tool allows symphonies the identical signature of hooting owls, thunderclaps, wavelets, lover's sighs--expressions never articulated through artistic interpretation suddenly became available to amazed audiences, hearing variants in an orginal's precise register; whether these renditions were serious or comic, they evoked powerful thoughts and emotions, the esthetic test. But such innovation might also enable the uterine world to experience sonoral adaptations from its own environment, the reorchestrated native anthem flooding that amphitheater in which the front-row concertgoer would miss not a single note.

As shown by **Figure III**, engineering this experiment was easier than writing its score (the hardwiring edge software inevitably suffers). First, placental parameters of sound had to be established by digitally sampling numerous examples--not just Hajime Murooka's but later recordings which captured the imprinting crescendo of maternal blood penetrating the placenta.

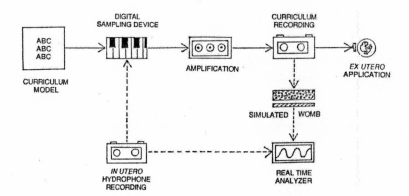

Figure III

SONIC STIMULI GENERATION

77

Once translated to an electronic format, subtle departures from that sonic cornerstone were constructed, with these altered in pitch and clarity so when transmitted back through the mother's abdominal wall they would arrive pulsing precisely like their primary source. For further adjustments, to avoid repeated cervical intrusions by hydrophone, an artificial womb was fabricated whose attenuating qualities matched those of the intervening tissue and fluid, about a 30-decibel difference. Finally, fidelity could be assured through use of a real time analyzer which visually contrasted the derivative wave forms with their natural archetype, controlling volume for safety while speaking the regional dialect.

Yet what would constitute credible departures from the acoustic experience every fetus receives? As elucidated before, one guide was unmistakable: Like all developmental dynamics, knowledge is by definition progressively attained--this incremental effect educates only to the extent new information references old in a recognizable manner, paralleling the epigenetic mechanism of organic and inorganic growth, human or crystalline; a curriculum denotes that distinctive way learning transpires--the stairstep *pantomeme*--whereas regressive or devolutionary processes undo sense, which is why cosmic and organismic entropy are culturally defied. At physical peril when pausing, our ancestors had to rapidly master this lesson like the swiftest equilibrists, deciding on an endless tightrope between lesser and greater risk.

While our innate appetite for the new (what cat more curious, or reincarnative?) explains wanderlusts of body and mind--fidelities, infidelities--it occupies special dimension before birth . . . particularly because we now understand that the womb is no subdued cocoon but a seething cauldron where early senses stir biochemistry, manufacturing plant of giant presses stamping out neurogenetic templates in earsplitting tympany; agitation may be the perfect response initiating a search for less nonsense and more relevant language--touching elemental personality with imprintable pertinence. In fashioning each brick civilization required, this intrinsic education laid the carefully mortared groundwork for a cultural edifice which through intricate corridors and ornate chambers has fast outgrown its original architecture, an anteroom to cosmic scope: Courtesy of the digital sampling device, interesting departures from the redundant rule could be provided, beyond no longer sufficient nutrition a full course menu designed for the nascent brain.

Nonetheless, although science's acute ear, the hydrophone, had faithfully reported what sounds flood every pregnant abdomen, indicating with inescapable persuasion a repetitious matriarchal decree as that rudimentary pattern whence all subsequent order derives, there was one covert contender for primacy in initiating structure which continued to intrigue this experimenter--namely, fetal cardiation. If the human heart inaugurates its vigorous movements scarcely weeks following conception, swelling so fast that shortly later the pulses (at first greater, then averaging a prenatal rate roughly twice as rapid as the mother's) visibly shake the diminutive being like a jackhammer, surely another powerful force was present, potentially of imprintable importance: Within the tiny frame elementary mental registration--for a creature already demonstrating multisensory fitness--must take place. And what of that maternal cardiac baseline in women which, due to anxiety over their pregnancy, rises well beyond average--some as much as by half?

It was fascinating to consider why prenatal and neonatal electroencephalography[2] detects protoalpha or slow-wave activity at rates almost identical with those produced by the resting maternal as well as fetal heart, approximately one to two hertz (cycles per second). The key question: Do these sources serve as our earliest instructors, not imparting just repetitious content but the actual morphology of its perception? Even if there appeared only erratic correspondence between cardiac and cortical cycles attending other vertebrates,[3] had nature evolved

---

[2] Recording electrical evidence of data traffic throughout the brain, a phenomenon discerned from 43 days gestational age.

[3] Possibly since alpha state--awake yet quiescent, with no visual input-- requires volunteers, nonhumans therefore restrained, blindfolded, or

twin governors for our first environment so that through example akin to sympathetic vibration mental neurology commenced oscillating, sensory receptors still being developed though already routing the simplest yet recurring messages along barely traceable pathways where terminals increasingly sparked in temporal mimicry of the stimulatory causes?

Nowhere across the professional literature was I able to track this creative relationship (which is not altogether remarkable since at close range history repeatedly zigzags, leapfrogging whole steps of knowledge, with science beggared no less than other disciplines)--it had simply been overlooked. After years surmising some precise causation to my main idea--a critically missing link in what seemed for colleagues an otherwise complete concept--even preparing an unavoidable experiment, at last I located two papers which identified with conclusivity the principle such efforts had sought; they are noted by Leonard George, in *Alternative Realities*:

> The power of sound in banishing our ordinary sense of reality is based on a direct impact of auditory stimulation on the human nervous system. This effect is known as auditory driving.
>
> The electrical activity of the neurons in the brain tend to be rhythmic, as revealed by the wavelike paterns of EEG readings. The natural pattern of activity is susceptible to influence by rhythmic sensory input; brain cells tend to fire in synchrony with repetitious sounds.
>
> Walter and Walter, in their early work on the related phenomenon of photic driving, speculated that brain activity could also be driven by the rhythmic "sound such as that produced by an untuned percussion instrument or an explosion." Neher exposed subjects to rhythmic drumming sounds, while monitoring their EEG activity. He found that

---

drugged, thus yielding waveforms of but approximately comparative merit; however, see William Klemm's EEG tables in *Biology Data Book*, edited by Philip Altman and Dorothy Dittmer, 1973, also the *Merck Veterinary Manual*, 1991, under "physiological values."

the neural firing of every subject conformed to the frequency of the drumming.

Auditory driving--that explanatory mechanism (which M. G. Rosen and J. Scibetta would confirm a few years after Andrew Neher's 1961 discovery) addressed each factor in the equation connecting curricularized prebirth sonic stimulation, imprinting, fetal apoptosis, EEG increase, and superlative postnatal achievement; the innovation involved--technology not less than thesis--was basically an auditory driver inducing our fundamental data-management rate to a faster, more sophisticated level (perhaps attaining incrementally a qualitative or deep ecological state, according to the Santiago cognition model), axiomatically of survival value on the fitness landscape, functional because invoked before cell death when neurogenesis can respond to organismic resourcefulness solicited for a lifetime.

Of prime importance appears sonic stimulation's effect upon synapses while originating, with neuronal interface directly impacted by how often messages occur--the electrochemical traffic either passing or parked. Peter Huttenlocher offers this explanation from a 1994 perspective:

> Changeux proposed a theory of selective stabilization of developing synapses, which relates the persistence of early synapses to the formation of functional neuronal networks. The schema has the underlying assumption that many early synaptic contacts are made randomly. During early stages of synaptogenesis, many more contacts are formed than persist in the mature state. Some of these early labile contacts become incorporated into functioning units or circuits as electrical activity develops in the system. These circuits are thought to be established through the effects of afferent activity from sense organs on the developing central neurons, as well as through the formation of intrinsic neural circuits. According to this view, synapses that are incorporated into functonal units become stabilized, while those not incorporated become inactive and are eventually

81

resorbed. The presence of electrical activity in the developing system is essential for the stabilization of some synaptic contacts and elimination of others.

Recent computer simulations of neural networks suggest that this mechanism for establishment of order in a chaotic system is at least feasible. They show that a considerable degree of organization can be imposed on a system that initially has random connections, provided the system is subjected to incoming signals that have repeating patterns.

The last sentence offers perhaps the key rationale why prenatal enrichment by recurring, curricularized sound works.[4] Yet which stimulus prevailed: the slower though deafening average parental beat--occasionally accelerated by gestation--or the offspring's faster if own corporeal measure; how might so tentative an instrument discriminate difference, and was there danger in introducing *another* pacemaking presence? Surprisingly, the answer to these core questions lay in the fact of a necessary cerebral defense.

For maintaining existence in our perilous environmental niche, from its historical inception the nervous system's command center was required to track concurrent events--fewer at the invertebrate level, distinctly busy among human progenitors: this handiwork at fireside, that noise outside the

---

[4] An acoustic speculation: Might primitive dances involving gravidae, replete with percussive orchestration typically increasing the beat over not inconsiderable periods of time--roughly progressive and imprinting--have amounted to crude but somewhat influential fetal stimulation? Were corresponding brainwave changes in the unborn responsible for survival features so important that, once genetically discerned, the improvements proved heritable--Lamarckism valid only prebirth? If an enclave of our species observed no similar rituals, would its fate be sealed (did Neandertals lack rhythm, drums)? Further, given that the tempo of television and radio speech or music has considerably accelerated over the last decades, with babies in utero inundated by these soundbursts, might the resultant auditory driving be responsible for the same period's Flynn effect? Beyond a plethora of conjecture, musicologists, anthropologists, neuroanatomists, geneticists, and evolutionary psychologists may wish to entertain interdisciplinary pursuits along these lines.

cave . . . an intimate sphere bounded by a predatory perimeter. Thus we learned to subliminally monitor surroundings while asleep, but also dream when awake--letting imagination leap from the moment, an everpresent challenge for teachers; conversely, such inborn governance also blanks out the classroom clock which can tick with infernal immediacy through an examination, ignores a noisy neighbor, lets the commuter read, reduces radio or television to white noise behind primary conversation, the sheepdog's vision similarly compensating hirsute interference. A further ancient need for simultaneous monitoring would protect against threats from different directions--vigilance of an Argus was required in battle--the stalker's prey stealthily pursued by others quite willing to feast upon a fellow diner.

Applicable to our purpose, Mac Freeman has compellingly described bilevel appreciation by the fetus as duocentric, perceiving self *and* the external world from the outset, therefore also letting formative focus steer around omnipresent cardiac patterning and seize upon relevant novelty--the identical acumen of Anthony DeCasper's subjects, who demonstrated keen infant reactions to material spoken during gestation, or those studied by Annette Karmiloff-Smith, at University College, London, confirming linguistic morphology after birth that had been acquired in utero.

A not unreasonable expectation was that departures from content at the academic entry point, temporally reinforced for imprinting, if familiar enough to register but still minimally altered could by testing discrimination skills multiply the first data storage sites and connecting circuitry.[5] The epigenetic principle had been expressed with cosmic sweep by that polymathic structuralist, D'Arcy Thompson:

---

[5] Objection among theorists and researchers has resisted the physical fixing of memory (perhaps revising their views at the 1996 finding for this very gene in the rodent hippocampus; see J. Z. Tsein *et al.*, and T. J. McHugh *et al.*) yet analogy or metaphor are the only ways language can define function, in fact anything--even numbers are so explained.

. . . number, order and position are the threefold clue to exact knowledge; . . . these three . . . furnish the "first outlines for a sketch of the Universe."[6]

Should this curricularized input commence before the precise instant adult prejudice decrees as inaugurating consciousness (like medieval disputes over angelic density on pinhead, a moot point since sensory skill routing signals to the formative brain is measured in degree practically from conception, interoceptively, under sonic wavefronts breaking over the skin's nervous surface, or by virtue of bone conduction to preauditory receptors), it would nonetheless evoke chemical and electrical responses which forge evolving familiarity--an ability continuing throughout fetal sleep. Later in term, the unborn child's wakeful awareness might momentarily start at this ex utero stimuli, and then react to their tempo with approximately cadenced limb movement or regularized breathing of fluids--commencing on average about midterm--yet subsequent boredom (clinically called habituation) could shift overt attention without interrupting secret receptivity, the brain developmentally primed for deepest steerage despite upper deck activity: Neurogenesis hungers for order it can utilize in constructing that microcosm which in commensurate measure-- as accorded by environmental niche requirements--mirrors the universe, and will not stop until feedback ceases . . . earlier from an unenriched environment or due to programmed fetal apoptosis when the brain's first set of blueprints is finished. Alert or asleep, unless severely damaged the organic computer is destined to learn.

Like time outside quantum electrodynamics, there can be but one direction: The lesson plan must proceed from simple to complex. Because fetal heartbeat runs more rapidly than the mother's pulse it should constitute a secondary resource--as the louder material presence and most fundamental information

---

[6] In a recent interview, sonic impresario Vangelis Papathanassiou expressed the principle behind his profession:

Music dominates the universe. It is the prime force, it has given shape to space.

provider hers claims precedence--with extrapolations built upon that maternal resting rate of nearly one instance every second, not two like the tiny organ maintains. Upon realizing this, I then extracted another meaning from the same clue: These separate rhythms, naturally impregnated in the developing brain, already introduce an alphabet, however elementary. Gravidic cardiation signifies the onset of a new life's first paradigm--more permanently implanted than any other--at once opposed by its absence, the silence between strokes, together establishing *a baseline binary language*. And the prenatal blood pump inscribes an additional letter in this infant primer, 100 percent speedier than memory's initial rate. In short, by its opening month--with hormonal, visceral, and protosensory learning fully under way--the fetus has in fact complete all academic requirements toward the opening phase of a lifetime utterly dependent upon this groundwork; but nature's neurogenetic expectation for *Homo sapiens* is evolutionarily not much beyond that given to the other primates, creatures totally trapped in habituation zones by their biology--an explanation for like behavior among these similarly endowed species . . . including us at remnant atavistic moments, just as we indulge token altruism.

Over that duration which constitutes the imprinting minimum, then, should our earliest cultural education introduce nothing but a series of one-second advances from the template? There were two main objections to this proposal: First, if proceeding by whole-integer sequences, the adult brainwave's basic rate (alpha state about ten cycles per second, attained at puberty) would arrive in but a few jumps, perhaps too mature for an unborn child thus, like Mozart's virtuosities, blurring to background noise; and a major technical difficulty could not be surmounted--compressing sonic repetitions within an extremely short timeframe while maintaining each note's perceived distinction, which included a critical trailer element of diminishing as well as descending tone. But by creating subtler shifts in pace, horizontal sequences advancing a quarter or half hertz, greater yet more closely related variety might through auditory driving wean the womb's resident from its chronic mindset to what our replacement paradigm required: faster, more efficient data-handling, expanded experience, extended memory. A strictly cardiac curriculum was being reconceptualized as derivationally cortical.

Even so, could the tone changes of an extremely abbreviated musical scale also interest developing mind--since between fetal and maternal heartbeat there were limited but discernable vertical differences? Although many months typically pass before lullabies become dependable sleep inducements, investigations by Anthony DeCasper and Peter Hepper had revealed that newborns exposed prebirth to the simplest melodies evince rapt attention upon hearing them. Toward full-term gestation's end a certain appreciation of pitch must pertain--especially should it be built upon an accelerating temporal repertoire. The morphological example seemed clear, as James Shreeve points out in his 1996 article, "Music of the Hemispheres": Tune builds upon tempo, the measure antedates its harmonics. And as long as the principle of auditorily driving fetal neurology was maintained, certainly there would be virtue for parental eavesdroppers in overlaying a slight melodic line, since postnatal music never sounds like Morse code.

These considerations, with less attractive candidates, occupied me during a few preparatory years until an obliging mother possessed with pragmatic foresight stepped forward; she was curious about prelearning theory, and--newly pregnant-- wished to evaluate it herself. Since our prehistoric debut, never from future vantage had an opportunity been so welcome.

Chapter Eight--*Proof Positive*

When a new candidate for paradigm is first
proposed, it has seldom solved more than a few
of the problems that confront it, and most of
those solutions are still far from perfect . . . .
Ordinarily, it is only much later, after the new
paradigm has been developed, accepted, and
exploited that apparently decisive arguments . . .
are developed. Producing them is part of normal
science, and their role is not in paradigm debate
but in postrevolutionary texts.

Thomas S. Kuhn, *The Structure*
of Scientific Revolutions, 1970[1]

Truths dawn diversely: Some startle skepticism as abruptly
as their waking premonition at midnight, others accrue by dream,
creeping to climax marginally noted--perhaps long after the
secret fact; an Archimedean eureka may resound skward or
sputter, then rebound in either direction. For its innovator an
hypothesizing winter suddenly over, this discovery waxed
brighter than an overdue spring sun.

The uniquely designed sonic progressions had been recorded
as a series of audiocassettes for administering twice daily in one-
hour sessions through binaural headphones applied across the
maternal abdomen; the incrementally more complex patterns--
advancing in tempo and pitch--were to be introduced over
weekly intervals. Testing at the fastest rate detected neither fetal
tachycardia nor cardiac arrhythmia, permitting the project to
commence under physician control with careful monitoring of
every aspect this original research could conceive. Following
earlier than usual movements, by midterm the volunteered infant
began softly responding with limb activity mimicking the

---

[1] Kuhn's use of "paradigm" for physics and related sciences has been lately
criticized by Steven Weinberg, who defers judgement about its application
to biology and behavior; such relevance is unchallenged here.

patterned stimuli, soon expecting these sequences at their scheduled hour or its arms and legs would vigorously remind the mother; her baby's head regularly sought the source of sound, listening as closely as possible.

In July 1987 a child was born demonstrating no isolated asset but all the superogatory features which previously distinguished fetally enriched neonates (see Chapter Four)--now packaged so parents would not have to improvise methods, assume their effectiveness and safety, or pursue tedious techniques; the auspicious debut signified what would shortly prove the first consistent elevation in human proficiency deriving from culturally enhanced neurogenesis. By producing an environmentally insisted response, evolution's niche logistics, this breakthrough intervention raised in terms both qualitative and quantitative the mark against which mental acumen leading to moral actions would henceforth be measured . . . another step toward a speciational dynamic our myths have long deified.

When human flight was first sustained over North Carolina dunes, no sober witness could have questioned what it would take history years to officially sanction; meeting philosophic and physical criteria for unalloyed veracity, a *Kitty Hawk singularity* should legitimize any inaugural event. *O, innocent onlooker!* Because even intrinsic senses and credentialed sensibility often deceive us, scrupulous verification not essentially cynical must at least define doubt (to the modern mind every miracle is suspect until explained, repeatedy), algorithmic belief versus anecdotal inadequacy. In this instance ten pregnant mothers were recruited over a few months for the second phase of the pilot study. Anticipating accusations of undue influence, the selection process screened parents to assure neither genetic giftedness nor affluence, avoiding any superbaby expectation (only two families pursued postnatal education beyond a typical upbringing); an ethnic mix was also deemed desirable.

Again, the curricularized sounds evoked gentle movements by their wrapt listeners, marking time like metronomes yet variously though always resuming--for seconds, or continuously over many minutes--as though taste, discrimination, and character were genetically manifesting themselves already.

Birth, neonatal, and early infant features precisely paralleled that of the sole predecessor, but clearly outdistanced all aspects expressed by children receiving widely diverse prenatal sonic alternatives in the preceding years. As members of a congruent group, their multimodal benefits far surpassed those deriving from any other method alleging fetal amelioration.

The question of how to professionally assess these dozen exceptional peers (including the original child and one set of twins) was itself a challenge. Because egalitarian perspective does not wish to prejudge youth's eventual station--and since testing of the very young for the farther future had always been an ambiguous enterprise--the primary purpose in separating early acumen from its lack serves diagnostic needs recommending immediate therapy: Deficit is identified in order to either supplement the struggle toward an average or protect that status quo from degradation.[2] Traditional measurements like the Bayley, Denver, or Brazleton scales were never intended to identify excellence as grounds for academic speedup, just the opposite, and IQ cannot even be solicited until an age when responsive and articulation skills have been honed by schooling. But, as if on demand, a landmark professional instrument appeared.

Previous assays of human development concentrated upon motor or visual prowess--how soon an infant could crawl, toddle, and walk, or coordinate hand with eye movements--although these were less adequate for lengthier projections. But a new thesis proposed the brain's knack for trafficking in language as our most successful elementary prognosticator, way beyond birth's short-term Apgar scoring; predictive tests for older children are under one rubric or another based upon the same rationale, now neonatally introduced by progressive hospitals therefore tacitly acknowledging proficiency at that nascent level. From plotting on an axis of uniform linguistic stages a subject's

---

2 Unfortunately, programs assisting retarded students vastly exceed in quality and funding supplemental work assigned to the overqualified--who are assumed to be better equipped in fending for themselves--with only the former segregated lest an invested midground suffer.

receptive and expressive features--data routing through the cortical computer--up to age two years, later cognitive accomplishment could be correlated; what rewarded investigators was an incredibly revealing portrait of human facility during its embarkation, one from which lifetime prospect could be powerfully projected.

Constructed by Johns Hopkins University researchers under Arnold Capute, the Clinical Linguistic and Auditory Milestone Scale (CLAMS) observed numerous developmental signposts: when an infant initially coos, smiles, babbles, gestures, speaks words, and names body parts. While designed to detect those who require society's aid in surviving with impediments (the 1994 work of Purdue University psychologist Michael Lynch *et al.* indicates Down syndrome speech problems appearing by two months postbirth), this graphic format mapped the earliest mental terrain of our species in longitudinal profile without utilizing the biochemical cross-sections portrayed by physical dissection, tomography, or resonance imaging. Inside its widening wedge-- defined uppermost at the gifted boundary, population's top ten percent, and the same portion by the lower edge where deficiency prevailed--essentially each instance of Earth's highest consciousness would register . . . genius one extreme, imbecile the other; should an individual fall outside the definitive confines, they must exhibit an extraordinary difference, a distinction presumably valid for human history taken together since this morphology frequents world literature and legend. But when these generic calipers were applied to children prenatally empowered by the project (**Figures IV and V**), their placement astonishingly depicted maturation as though province for an audit not yet devised--that which would render the displaced norm more infantile than its chronological age described.

If unable to disparage a tester's academic dossier, professional suspicion confronting consistent anomaly next targets tools; so, lest observer objectivity be questioned, for various evaluations in the fetal enrichment study not every measure depended upon skills or behavior: Birthweight, length, and cranial circumference--irrespective of parental size or nutrition during pregnancy--identified substantial presence

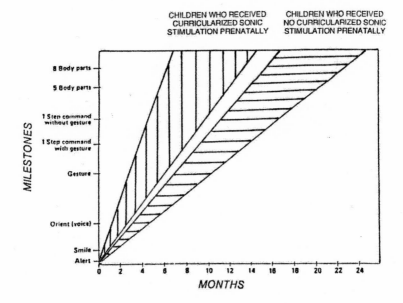

Figure IV

RECEPTIVE LANGUAGE DEVELOPMENT

91

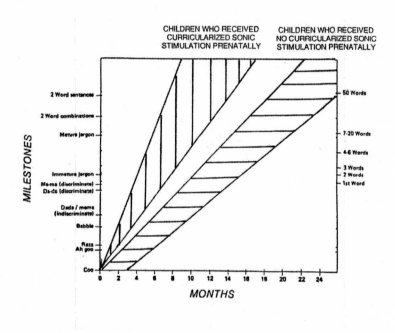

Figure V

EXPRESSIVE LANGUAGE DEVELOPMENT

among the largest percentage, suggesting increased motor activity in utero due to the stimulation had exercised responsive bodies and raised oxygen or other chemical levels; consequences generated by this heightened environmental input--originating outside the womb, and from an invigorated fetus--were putatively contributing to neurogenetic material beyond that restricting the head's traditional density. Still, these bigger babies were neither extending labors nor necessitating caesarean interventions; instead, the incidence was well below national averages.

One clever gauge of cognitive processing explains why blinking takes place--not just for clearing particles from the eye surface but also to signify when a qualitative conclusion is attained by the brain: Cerebral processing, either from sensory input or self-generated, accrues informational quanta until its summation commences another cumulative sequence, at which point ocular registration triggers lid movement. The adult rate per minute averages 15 (excepting that self-consciousness associated with deception), while newborns blink only once in two minutes . . . yet prenatally stimulated babies were at parturition achieving half the mature figure, their mental efficiency amassing and assessing experience like children years beyond such a preliminary stage.

Electroencephalography recorded alpha rhythm three months after birth resembling that of cortical profiles much older, the advantaged neurology absorbing and producing data at a level which vastly elaborated experience for this early point--an implicative feedback synergistically accelerating development.[3]

As the children entered school, stellar academic achievement supported by IQ scores centering on 150 verified no ephemeral but enduring virtues . . . confirming in reverse that lowest birthweight babies exhibit the highest incidence of gross mental deficit or deficient intelligence (see M. Richards, *et al.*).

---

[3] A computerized analysis published in 1983 by T. Gasser *et al.* demonstrates that EEG and intelligence are empirically linked, with delayed alpha indicative of retardation, and developmental advancement revealing elevated results from cognitive tests.

Controlled comparisons with music or other sonic material revealed only the above means to confer qualitative distinction upon postnatal existence: Parents might themselves prefer the classical composers, modern dance tunes, native chants, or New Age sounds (sometimes nature more pristinely digitized than authentic), yet none but temporal progressions in maternal heartbeat applied before birth could claim scientific credibility demonstrating comprehensive and consistent value; even the potentially best placebo effects during gestation were undetectable contrasted with this technology.[4] Recalling the idiosyncratic approaches families had intuitively undertaken a decade prior--all involving sound--isolated benefits appeared in various evaluations where increasingly complex music was administered during the last trimester; however, these mostly short-term outcomes barely merited statistical attention.

While further birth cohort pilot trials during the late 1980s yielded to randomized clinical assessments by independent professionals and facilities, the numbers of those prenatally acquainted with the innovation growing from hundreds to thousands, the hardest evidence started supporting what once seemed extravagant anecdotes; reported in the "Brave New Babies" television documentary--viewed by an audience of millions throughout many countries--a controlled study under Mikhail Lazarev's physician team at the Children's Rehabilitation Center, Moscow, showed substantial cognitive and social gains for this technology compared with maternal singing and classical music administered before birth. After 100,000 such children had joined families of usually modest means, demonstrating no negative factors concerning behavior, scholastic record, parental hopes, and health (developed country

---

[4] What should be an obvious argument against music's lasting gains for the fetus is that since most sounds, whether Mozart or Muzak, in the maternal surrounding also attend her unborn child (as confirmed by in utero hydrophone), and because expectant mothers in all cultures have been exposed daily to a melodic assault--from television, radio, CDs, cinema, workplace loudspeakers, dancefloor amplifiers--over decades, if this sonic onslaught yielded consistent prenatal benefits we would be witnessing an impressive generational outcome; alas, just not the case.

mortality rates from disease or accident alone should have meant a hundred or more normative deaths--instead, not one), in fact quite the opposite; amassing portfolios on their superlative activities became a staggering proposition.

By any measure the developmental upgrading case was made through unprecedented achievement displayed across a considerable population. Returning to the previous description of fetal apoptosis, it appeared outcomes were completely parallel with an evolutionary hypothesis validated under quantifiable theory: The protobrain was being demonstrably fortified before that almost total shutdown accompanying full-term birth (**Figure VI**), and the ensuing resource would positively affect the individual's entire life--like any survival asset--just as its deprivation condemns retardates to marginal existence, minimal expectation, perhaps dementia, also encouraging early mental decline among those born with intellectual capacity but slightly substandard.

Either solo or for a group, how is progress defined? In the person, tradition heeds a complex of physical, psychological, emotional, social, educational, and spiritual factors, with accumulation attaining an ethereal plateau named adulthood from which slippage at the senior end can signal reversion to infant behavior--Shakespeare's hardly arbitrary ages of man; collectively applied, this morphology excited Vico, Spengler, Toynbee, Darwin, and Teilhard de Chardin.[5] However, the issue deserves further perspective.

First we must understand that the concept of improvement dates from no more than several centuries--astonishing when their few generations in lucky countries have come to view bettering life's minimal requirements as an inevitability constrained only by lack of effort (upon greater global interface, even some among the Third World's impoverished throngs are starting to sense a determinable destiny attending not just outside

---

[5] Daniel Dennett views the latter two as methodological poles, unreservedly critical of Teilhand failing logic far more relaxed than that serving the Jesuit's own stringent order; yet a general thematic complement can be inferred.

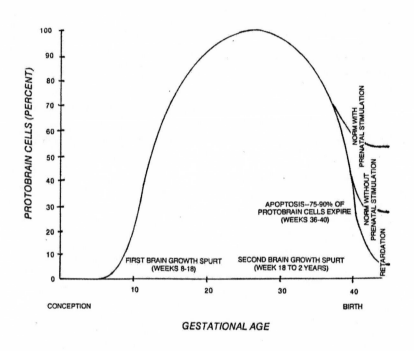

Figure VI

PROTOBRAIN CELL DEATH MODIFICATION

96

affluence); the Industrial Revolution, fueled from linear engineering, made fortunate children then and much vaster numbers now believe their own maturation was synonymous with that of civilization--one's consciousness represents the historical period it inhabits, each simultaneously rising. Indeed, supporting this newfound optimism, certain meanings for the word *develop*--evolve, emerge, expand--propose an open process, not restricted to a midground such as *over*develop implies. While semantic latitude remains taboo to the hardest sciences, limits can also provide guidance when searching for parametric axes or categories; without intending bacterial offense, cavils against the concept of progress have been deservedly discredited by W. Ford Doolittle: "Mozart really is more complicated than *E. coli*."

How to frame, then formulate both eschatological question and answer comprising the human Rorschach? Two broadest guidelines mark the path. If an apparent commonplace for ability in *Homo sapiens*, imbecilic and gifted describe the extremities of a span most of us inhabit about its center.[6] When identifying less complex life, cerebration insists with the inescapable bias of self-proclaimed yet also genetically conferred authority that there are not merely theoretical pretexts for discerning its lack . . . or extrapolation; faculties other than intelligence certainly exist, but these are to a significant extent in evolutionary terms, a material and mental spectrum comprised of

---

[6] While *Darwin's Dangerous Idea* impeccably argues its main contentions, also mounted by Dennett is a sagacious defense of lesser skills: Simplistically reasoned analyses are better than none--sophomoric effort may outweigh the venerably moronic--or excessive finesse indecipherable to an intelligent but lay observer; nor can quantum physics escape allusion. Another requisite banality: Predicating the path to linguistic sophistication, all states and things assume identity from their opposites (being/nonbeing, positive/negative, cold/hot, up/down, love/hate, pro/con) before undergoing separation or contrary linkage, dualism's nuanced demise, with meaning based far more upon emotionally interpreted experiences than is admitted; an absolute relativity--particular as well as gross, perceived or real even though synonymous--therefore touches development with temporal precision of utmost pertinence.

dependent upon quantifiable neurology. If growth is visualized sequences commencing at the Big Bang and pointblank en passant, then just as milestones chart organismic aging so benchmarks--formerly biologic, now cultural--clock consciousness through its accruing guises.

From this perspective, the vertical measure in **Figure VII**, though generalized, is less metaphoric than empiric: the combined value of an organism at time's developmental strata. (My depiction lengthens the vectors of **Figures IV and V**, beyond two years flattening their learning curves since data acquisition never again occurs at its earliest rate--when the ex utero cosmos is first encountered and appreciation correspondingly explodes, with that degree heavily determined by fetal precedent.) A characterological sum, composed of whatever features the observer selects--I favor consciousness-- allows contrast with peers or between lifeforms. The chart delineates how enrichment after a birth preceded by no extra stimulation strains an upper neurological limit: The intensively trained superbaby (without prenatal curricularized sonic exposure), frequent subject of parental ego disappointed at its own shortcomings, may initially respond if genetic background grants yet later resist with debilitating behavior--usually during adolescence, a burnout sometimes spiralling from drugs to suicide--should typical though now evolutionarily displaced potential prevail . . . accounting for that clinical brilliance which can earn genius an asocial reputation. Conversely, when before birth a child has capacity increased by cortical empowerment, expanding culture's niche, the ceiling of innate ability extends further than what restricts mainstream contemporaries-- irrespective whether the norm is saturated with postnatal blandishments. Overstimulation applies where appetite--inherent or induced--exceeds competence, for this reason a constraint only outside the womb; because neurogenetic learning responds solely to that which imprints--with every other sound or synesthetic alternative therefore white noise--the issue of excessive enrichment cannot arise during gestation, while its

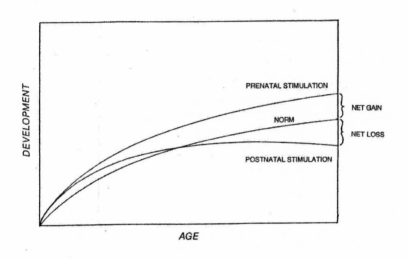

Figure VII

LIFETIME PERFORMANCE

zerobased fetal format allows rapid pattern acceptance and assimilation . . . through the dynamic of auditory driving.

Although numerous impressive proofs, all utilizing recognized assessments professionally substantiated over a decade, were to encourage commercialization for an obviously interested world, controlled investigative refinements adopting brain imaging techniques are being solicited; these will feature definitive contrast agents by which the speed or location of newborn mental response to assorted stimuli can be identified in motion and intensity, thus discounting subsequent influence (since cerebral functions require energy, this technology tracks where and how much metabolic change varies--by consuming glucose or oxygen--the physical art of thinking).

Besides resonance and tomographic scans, another cutting-edge empiric evaluation is electroencephalography applied immediately after birth to include neural network computer analysis, then tracking basal information-processing rates until the children attain puberty, when alpha rhythm traditionally attains its adult resting frequency of ten hertz. Most definitive, however, would be the possibility that sequenced sonic enrichment--as a key environmental influence during the neural window of maximum plasticity preceding massive cell death at gestation's end--might favorably modify the genetic structure itself, an hypothesis explored in this book's paired volume. If verified, 1998 evidence for DNA associated with intelligence, alertness, and curiosity could suggest neonatal sampling to compare such presence. Employing these newly designed approaches along with older and any forthcoming instruments, double-blind examinations--across the fullest range of protocols --from reputable institutions are strongly encouraged, complementing current research in various countries.

By the 1990s (auspiciously during that period American governmental proclamation had decreed as Decade of the Brain), an affordable product parents could rely upon with complete confidence for its safe engagement of the fetal protobrain, facilitating their baby's earliest educational opportunity, became available worldwide. Nothing else, neither technique nor technology, was accomplishing the neurogenetic upgrade whose exemplary record in resolving individual and group problems should direct human destiny even beyond the newborn millennium.

Chapter Nine--*A Tool for These Times*

> The orthodox theory musn't *presuppose* any
> process of directed mutation . . . but it can leave
> open the possibility of somebody's discovering
> nonmiraculous mechanisms that can bias the
> distribution of mutations in speed-up directions.

> Daniel C. Dennett, *Darwin's Dangerous Idea*, 1995

Matter's indigenous resonance, the incessant melody
spinning atoms and galaxies, that liveliest music driving diatoms
or vertebrates, has in its mortal score been further orchestrated--
but by the instrumentalists themselves, for a change freeing these
creative creatures from an accomplished though aging conductor,
the biologic maestro. With their cosmic song engineered at
faster frequency, nothing short of the impressionable universe
stands to gain: If an omnipresent heat death was programmed
from time's birth, by diminishing cellular demise in our nascent
brain we can seek to resist and even restructure with careful
panache this indifferent fate, now theoretically, later materially,
the same should physical expansion continue forever. Culture is
infectuous--irresistible when hearkening to the heart.

Behind the one clinically secure and consistently worthwhile
prenatal stimulation resource--technology displacing whatever
other activities parents might initiate--resided a twofold
stipulation: Evidence gathered over ten years of testing showed
that for optimal reception by the fetus sonic parameters found in
utero had to be scrupulously observed, with curricularized
adaptations from imprinted maternal bloodpulses the only steps
for engaging incipient neurology at the sole stage which could
substantially offset the massive cortical decease concluding full-
term pregnancy.

All outside this strict definition appeared relatively
meaningless for unborn children; because of surprising
information about the uterine world, it stood to revised reason

102

that a mother's voice or music transmitted wombward by intent mattered little if most sounds in her environment were anyway attending the fetus--these rhythmically capricious therefore not imprintable--arriving inside only to encounter the ceaseless cardiac crescendo resounding throughout. The clear distinction was that such influences constitute essentially *random* stimuli, uncoded for neurogenetic durability, accelerating or decelerating with no auditory driving capability, axiomatic nonsense to an infant who had not even begun ascending the rudimentary stairs of its culture . . . whereas the internal hematic tones served as that zerobase from which gradually progressive input could commence in a derivative vocabulary.

Paralleling this contention, in 1999 separate studies by Christopher Chabris at Harvard Medical School, and Kenneth Steele of Appalachian State University, seriously challenged Frances Rauscher *et al.*, finding no significant gains for either abstract reasoning or spatial thinking due to any alleged effect from classical music; pleasure for audience and artist certainly, an immediate placebo gain perhaps--but nothing that could be claimed a permanent brain booster. While these new findings applied to adults, the implication for fetal listeners was hardly without meaning.

Since not one other innovation meets the standards of appropriate science for our fundamental academic institution, the technology this investigation happened upon opens doors to a school which graduates only superlative achievers, the first verifiably *Gifted Generation*, ubiquitous sagacity charged with compassion, an empathic and polymathic commonplace. A tradename reflecting positive effect, understood where English prevails as the first or leading second language, was no semantic challenge: *BabyPlus.* (United States patent 6,494,719). The hardware translates to microchip those native stimuli which when generated outside the womb enter its interior speaking a tongue exclusively inflected for that locus; the attenuating effect of abdominal thickness has been taken into account, and sonic volume is reduced below the in utero heartbeat's standard din.

Two formats were introduced during the last decade. Household batteries power an anatomically contoured unit whose sixteen numbered program buttons are activated with a single switch, each selection advancing in tempo from the placental blood norm through quarter-hertz increments; the final rhythm slightly exceeds half our brain's average adult alpha frequency, ushered there by the processes of auditory driving and imprinting. Equally sequential pitch elevations introduce qualitative changes in tone, a preparation for neonatal and infant melodies. An easily observed red light turns on when the energy source runs low, and escaping sound is diminished by a raised surface surrounding the speaker. Slightly larger than an electronic pager or pocket calculator, this lightweight apparatus clips to the waistband of clothing, alternatively attached with a thin belt or is contained in an abdominal pouch which contains two additional speakers. Ergonomic features comform to pregnancy's comfort requirements. The current model, shown in **Figure VIII**, features a small screen--directly visible by the mother when the unit is positioned on her abdomen--displaying program numbers with all sequences accessed by means of one button; this oval version replaces the rectangular one whose separate program keys were required to initiate less effective sonic patterns.

Just as I supplied American patent and copyright offices with their original files documenting the history, hypotheses, theory, and practice of prenatal stimulation, in 1987 the United States Food and Drug Administration headquarters was approached about not federally regulating the first fetal learning technology. Since unborn children experience nearly every sound from the maternal environment, and this device simply curricularizes a natural rhythm, it was understood without objection to constitute an academic tool, jurisdictionally outside medical or healthcare parameters, and is so identified; also, from political perspective, denying the womb's pupil teaching by its own family would be as impossible as restricting adjacent parental conversation--the sheer logistics of which should discourage even those governments which gloss over human rights.

The invention is accessible worldwide through retail outlets, department stores, maternity shops, hospitals, and clinics, with mail order as well as Internet purchasing on many websites (see

Figure VIII

FETAL ENRICHMENT TECHNOLOGY

Glossary); it has been approved by the Juvenile Products Manufacturers Association. In addition to continuous software research, functional and cosmetic considerations of the physical housing receive ongoing attention; because pirated versions invariably lack the most recent advances, including important safety features, parents are strongly advised to locate authorized outlets. An essential project incorporating recycled and lower-cost materials is to design a model that operates on solar or mechanical energy--like the new South African windup radio, which from just a few handcranks can run nearly an hour--ideal for areas where batteries are difficult to obtain or are subject to high humidity and temperature; federal participation throughout the Third World will be sought for distributing the product so that its next youth can devise locally evolved solutions to mounting problems (rather than relying upon outside assistance from interests often with self-serving agendas), yet equally capable of multicultural contact demanding advanced linguistic and technical skills. Thousands of units have already been contributed to nations like China and Russia, whose wellbeing should immeasurably swell from human resources capable of creating more with less while accessing information which has become abstruse but nonetheless crucial in forging Earth's increasingly interrelated family.

This very goal defines the technology's claim to provisional ultimacy, for if we can vault--with talents never so pervasively prodigious--those present and promised hurdles that litter our path toward not just material prosperity but a richness of purpose, then all previous assistance pales; toward these ends it becomes the latest and leading factor in the evolutionary algorithm, for this moment selection pressure's foremost necessity, what two millennia back Vitruvius would likely have included as an "essential invention," the serendipitous spawn of pernicious times. Fire, stone axe, agriculture, money, threshing machine, movable type, telescope, steam turbine, postage stamp, internal combustion engine, airplane, rocket, electric light, telephone, radio, television, vaccine, nuclear power, computer, biochip . . . none of these discoveries has helpful or durable utility without conscientious vision executing their intent; taken together they may constitute a civilization but lack personal meaning without empathic intelligence: Such perspective can only arise from minds larger than self, that rational faith or soulful wisdom capable of soothing anguish while constructing heaven.

A crossroads has emphatically been reached, neither overdue nor premature, when yesterday's focus bores beyond endurance, and the infinite future looms like an instant no more stoppable than another passing with this sentence's end--despite Cassandric forecasts (see Samuel Huntington's *The Clash of Civilizations*, or Morris Berman's *The Twilight of American Culture*). Here and now, because it must, this discovery answers every remedial question relevant to our transformative moment: The prenatal stimulation breakthrough addresses historically relative ineptitude by facilitating a neurogenetic enterprise whose outcome will enhance the character and context of every tomorrow. At the rate today's Gifted Generation is proliferating, a standard globalist Hazel Henderson noted should soon be met:

> It's clear from history that an initially small group of determined people (less than 5 percent of a population) can leverage change in whole societies.

Unprecedented talent and vision added to an innate vigor would be sufficient for planetary transformation, a "revolution in the sphere of human consciousness" urged before the U.S. Congress in February 1990 by Czech Republic President Václav Havel. More than ever, our world literally begins in the womb.

107

Chapter Ten--*Stimulating Steps*

The more difficult and numerous the design
problems presented by an animal are, the more
complex it will be and the more elegant the
solutions will appear.

Michael French, *Invention and Evolution*, 1994

Although extolling conveniences unimagined during the
early lives of whoever reads these words, modernity leaves little
moment to sample its amply advertised wares: Fiscal forces
driven by runaway demographics typically force couples to work
longer hours, with single women in still sexist societies facing an
even more strenuous struggle--then aggravated when pregnancy
taxes their unequal income. And as the undeniably attractive
option is discovered that in utero stimulation will colossally
profit offspring, how might a contemporary parent spare the time
needed to convey an imprintable education for their prebirth
infant--reciting the required but rudimentally repetitious sounds
hour after hour? This dilemma, also concern over suitable sonic
volume and tone, determined why uniform technology had to be
developed--effectively, responsibly, urgently; if informed
commitment in a disastrously wanting world insists newcomers
are optimized, then the fortunate fetus deserves nothing less than
competitive fairness.

While the resulting ease of operation for BabyPlus can be
readily recapitulated from its instruction manual, related matters
and implications merit the following remarks; they are perforce
generalized, with individual lifestyles and contingencies
predominating. Although today's demands on mere existence
mean survivors cannot avoid being versatile, an unborn's
cognitive receptivity is so eager for pattern beyond the maternal
bloodpulse that it will soon relate to whatever input makes
comparative sense--which accounts for fetal recognition of the

curricularized sounds by regularized breathing or limb movement. Responding to this appetite, then, one fervent suggestion: *The more prenatal stimulation the better--earlier in term, greater daily exposure*; fear of excessive application ignores omnipresent cardiac noise pulsing considerably louder, also the mother's substantial acoustic environment filtering through, which are without doubt no inhibitors to fetal sleep, nor sustained hyperactivity inducements. And if "never too late" remains a prudent guideline, comprehensive trial protocols showed benefits trailing off should the practice commence during the last month of gestation, after week thirty-six.

Additional advantage--but no quantum leap beyond those superlative skills derived from commencing two months later-- may accrue if a mother starts stimulating before her second trimester begins, at fourteen weeks, presumably reflecting the extent of fetal auditory development, neural organization, and imprinting receptivity. Whenever the technology is introduced, its program changepoint can be ascertained from dividing the remaining number of days until an infant's due date by sixteen, the total sonic variants involved; a convenient agenda runs from weeks twenty to twenty-four, commencing a new lesson about every seven days. If prematurity occurs, enrichment from prior stimulation still results,[1] and should more seem desirable the unit may be wrapped in cloth to simulate the abdominal wall and continued near an incubator, while for a delayed birth the latter few programs are repeated. Initial evidence indicates that early use of the product may help stabilize pregnancies for those with miscarriage histories.

Minimum sessions of sixty minutes in length twice a day are advised, preferably separated by hours. Whether scheduled for morning, afternoon, evening, or night, *considerable value derives from establishing regular application times*, because the fetus will soon anticipate these meaningful events--its attention follows the stimulation clock far closer than adult presumption

---

[1] Normalization of breathing and heart rate among preemies through the use of music administered with miniature headsets has been observed in a 1995 hospital study by Steven Spedale.

might think possible. Again, no rigidity is decreed--not castiron rules to cause anxiety should the daily administration lapse, a program out of sequence be mistakenly selected, or the unit left behind while traveling--yet caring parents are often wearily aware that for children repeated activity helps distinguish chaos, the path from which constitutes our definitively ordered civilization; in the case of forgetfulness, just use sensible judgement and resume where the last session left off . . . the recipient brain will adjust with amazing versatility.

The speaker face can be situated under or over clothing anywhere on the mother's abdomen (see **Figure VIII**); to avoid developing skin sensitivity in one place, the location should be altered with each session, a maneuver which encourages the infant to shift position--its head typically follows the sound source. Shortly before delivery is expected, begin lowering the unit slightly day by day as a breech birth preventive, since the baby may elect to keep an ear near the descending stimuli. While offering her child its earliest scholastic education, the mother can with comfort engage in almost any pursuit except bathing or swimming; the device attends pregnant women at their offices or homes, driving, dining, exercising, relaxing. From an inner perspective, this portable schoolroom could well take precedence over all ex utero surroundings.

As emphasized earlier, among genetic contributions distinguishing species, pattern awareness ranks high, predominantly for *Homo sapiens* where it is interpreted by individual endowment--even at life's start; responsiveness to music, speech, or vibration before birth cues subjectively from recurrence of the underlying beat. In experiencing the technology's sonic progressions, infants exhibit commensurate physical movements--arms and legs marking the measure, regulated chest fluctuations anticipatory of breathing otherwise evident only during prenatal sleep--if someone along the bloodline has an emotional connection to music: They play an instrument, sing, dance, whistle, hum, or just like rhythmic listening. The necessary interdependence of nature and nurture, seminally in utero where parental inheritance interpreting our vestibular world shapes development to characterological

110

uniqueness, becomes evident upon examining this first reaction: While the majority of infants will orient heads toward the sound, others kick at it like a game, their temperament already manifest through active versus passive personalities.

Behaviorists claim habituation sets in when interest fastens upon a stimulus but soon stops, yet this insistence wholly ignores the special type of learning that predominates before birth; *if the maternal bloodpulse were entirely habituated it would not imprint*--as Lee Salk's observations found--which describes a constant though unconscious environmental monitoring by our interoceptive sense along with bitracking, that neuronal eavesdrop on covert events noted prior, the brain's multilevel perception evolved in an acutely survivalistic world. Not only does this cognitive model explain--irrespective of fetal habituation--the consistently gifted beneficiaries of curricularized sonic exposure, when specifically vigorous the unborn child's physical responses vary from seconds to minutes throughout a session, even studiously still until the source ceases (as if to request continuation) or shortly precede the appointed hour--signalling a state of readiness perhaps corresponding with the mother's anticipation, triggered chemically. Each longitudinal test has confirmed, however, that although a prenate may sleep through the stimulatory periods, sensory antennae must continue transmitting the structured data to its cortical receptors (see M. Cheour *et al.* for new evidence of infant learning while asleep) since postnatal scores are parallel with those demonstrating full alertness. What this diverse expression suggests is character differentiation far earlier in development than science previously recognized.

Extreme fetal motility causing physical discomfort to the mother is seldom encountered, and then only for an instant until the child alters position; late in term, a larger and stronger baby occupying space become smaller may maintain demonstrative arm or leg gestures which might encourage ceasing the session, an instance amplified with twins--or other multiples--but if the process was administered for at least several weeks its assistance will have been imparted. Should a mother start stimulating in the final trimester or begin soon after conception and feel more

111

cautious, she can commence slowly, just a few minutes daily with incremental increases until her confidence builds.

Once direct responses from the womb have been detected by parents, an eager question arises: Will other sonic material supplement that which my innovation offers? Because neurogenesis can only avail itself of information correlated with what has been indigenously imprinted--the continuous maternal and fetal heartbeats--curricularizing this language which defines deepest structure elaborates memory and discrimination skills; patterns falling outside these parameters are irrelevant, static simply bypassing the formative brain.

While mothers may share all safe activities with their prebirth baby and expect marginal placebo effects, real in utero importance should not be exaggerated; if they enjoy Haydn, haiku, philately, or pasta, pleasure signals might reach the fetus, though substantially enhanced lifetime accomplishment will not be an outcome. As generated by the new technology, imprinted stimuli never register inappropriately, but are appreciated by the protobrain for pertinence to the cardiac baseline; when early consciousness sleeps, the innovation's relevance continues--as does the maternal bloodpulse, alike in morphology yet also quite different from this monotonous pacemaker, an informational resource nature did not conceive until through evolutionary practice human perception elicited the response in counterpoint to environmental challenge. Such advice notwithstanding, parental enthusiasm seeking experimentation should heed a further cautionary note: Headphones vary considerably in quality, with audiocassette and compact disk players capable of sonic strength not always carefully controlled; by limiting its sounds below that of the womb's regular volume, this approach completely avoids danger to fetal hearing.[2]

---

[2] Significantly, no clinical studies report auditory impairment induced in utero except when pregnant mothers worked as jet engine mechanics or high-speed lathe operators experiencing extremely strong vibroacoustics; any contrary impressions are wholly erroneous--perhaps from misunderstanding popular treatments like the otherwise inspiring 1996 film, *Mr. Holland's Opus*, where a baby exposed in the womb to his father's love for music is, without credible correspondence, born deaf.

Much has been made of parent-child bonding by means of various techniques undertaken in pregnancy, yet multiple social inventories--administered neonatally, during infancy, and into the academic years--concretely validate that the expanding interaction through daily sonic involvement available from my system outweighs by a vast margin every other gestational attempt to strengthen the family unit. Since fetal growth remains in its earliest phases more a biochemical protocol stipulated genetically, only as neural sophistication evolves will the unborn child become an intimate player with the outside world; nonetheless, once initial maturity has been enhanced from prebirth stimulation, increased sensitivity toward sensory cues, including emotional messages, becomes the raised standard. For this reason, mother, father, siblings, grandparents, and friends may not merely witness limb responsiveness in the gesticulating prenate--by touching the maternal abdomen or observing these movements on ultrasound (especially when syncopated to the ex utero rhythms of BabyPlus)--but fetal rotation seeking proximity with the sonic source further reveals unsuspected ability; it therefore follows that those tactile games promoted by René Van de Carr are fitting adjuncts to my invention over the final trimester, both incorporated in Southeast Asia as part of the Nury Institute's comprehensive developmental program under physician Datin Noor Laily.

The communicative matrix which evolves while using this earliest learning tool can hardly be understated: With the unit employed twice or more each day, eliciting regularized internal receptivity whereby mothers--and other fascinated witnesses-- have verified a new person's most vital signals, those playful reactions already demonstrating enhanced consciousness, the interactive factor expands like pregnancy. An individual showing innately less defensiveness--rather than survivalistic self-interest inculcated by epochs of precultural fear--therefore a quicker and closer regard for others, reflects the ultimate effect from neurogenetic stimulation; postnatal observation repeatedly documents this empathic practice with an attitude approaching reverence. One occupationally liberating factor in these demanding times: The child's stronger affection generates

113

welcome parent choices, whether there are two incomes or single-mother employment, with no loss of family attachment from extensive daycare involvement.

This technology strives to assure that "birth itself is but an incident"--as D'Arcy Thompson drolly spoke--by extending experience before the fact so that a richer sense of involvement ensues, self-confidence secured neurologically prior to anxiety's official onset soon after delivery . . . hence the relaxed arrival, stressless curiosity, prolonged focus; open arms, hands, and eyes announce without the customary cry of anguish an advent beyond another demographic digit. While but alternating realms, a metamorphosis which transcends traditional ego has commenced, with its reverberations touching more shores than those from pebbles knowing only slight heights. To proudly celebrate this propitious occasion, many parents place the device nearby--hospital consenting--muffled by a towel for in utero fidelity, and played at the last-administered program; not surprisingly, the newborn's attention is riveted to this familiar source.

After the benefitted baby is born, high-contrast bedding, crib bumpers, mobiles, or toys afford the black-and-white antitheses early vision requires (sustenance circumscribing only nipple range); vivid colors come a few months later, then pastels, but the stark dualities of facial outlines, checkerboards, and concentric rings are initially prime, succeeded by geometric shapes, numbers, and letters. BabyPlus can be swathed in fabric to mimic the natural tones of the womb, and placed an infant's length away for reassurance, quieting, or sleep inducement over the postpartum weeks by using just the first program, exactly duplicating the maternal heartbeat's cadence when at rest; as stated before, to address prematurity the product may be similarly wrapped to continue all sequences until the original due date, mitigating genetically predetermined brain cell death which peaks about week forty (new findings reverse the old notion that minimal stimulation was best for babies delivered early--providing the source is sonic).

Beginning with birth, basic melodies or lullabies expand the curricular direction this child has grown to expect during

114

gestation. Whatever environmental enhancement parents offer prenatally primed youngsters, their special preparation enables intelligence to probe beyond the common, extracting more from those mundane dimensions than the rest of us could experience at an equivalent age; naturally, any resource will be appreciated further than nonstimulated peers can fathom, but the orthodox compulsion for purchasing expensive diversions may be resisted without guilt: A child fetally enriched by the new means simply makes more of less . . . to lasting personal and public gain.

If parents discover too late this fundamental learning aid, the desire for postnatally compensating their offspring is voiced with understandable concern; disturbing as it may first appear, since neuronal pruning has mostly transpired by birth, subsequent occasion for curbing this ultraconservative process does not exist: That deprived life's entire output will assume the formerly ordinary developmental profile. On the other hand, just as our most senior citizens (compared with whom astronaut Senator John Glenn remains a stripling) may not include those who could physically report from an extraplanetary perspective but their replacement did, so in these instances junior siblings receive what the timetable of scientific progress now schedules--yet become prolific founts for each family, including older brothers or sisters who missed the innovation's developmental window; *all* descendants today will rise to the level of cognition and ability their parents could not enjoy when young (which may be why computer game skills have upper age limits, just as abacus, typewriter, slide rule, or pocket calculator defined previous generations), even if the fetally advantaged can ascend faster and farther. Although tradition may object once youth is expected to outperform norms--a fear lately revived by the superbaby syndrome--because of neurogenetic optimization the combined mental, social, and creative faculties bearing upon situational demands hosts an extraordinary patience accompanying prowess: Coping without stress enables the enriched student to aid overburdened teachers as well as less capable classmates.

While special schools or accelerated classes for the consistently precocious are few, expensive, and typically prone to elitism (contrast John David Garcia's comprehensive curriculum presented in *Creative Transformation,* or *Transforming History*, by William Irwin Thompson), as with the above example these obstacles need not inhibit enterprise; talent ranging to genius has in achieving success generally fought on its own against staggering odds, and a perverse virtue of overcoming hurdles which daunt the less able is that struggle's pain. Even so, cyberspace already has advanced the learning curve to meet demands of exploration at unprecedented levels. In this regard, one fruitful feature of the philosophy surrounding BabyPlus is development of an optional computer network assisting communication among the children; for friendship, learning, or business they can contact others who were stimulated before birth, linking a highly enterprising community which should help steer the planet through precarious years. Connecting singular instances of giftedness strives to achieve that fissionable mass from which each participant can tap unbounded transpersonal powers, at the same time energizing those not fetally fortunate.

In essence, the technology's easily followed instructions vouchsafe tomorrow its positive potential; any parent may elect that alternative to a future plagued with fewer options, voting for perspicacious change through progeny capable of the task.

Chapter Eleven--*Progressive Ethics*

For all our apprehensions, we have no choice but to press ahead. We must do so, first, in the name of compassion. By turning our backs on technological change, we would be expressing our satisfaction with current world levels of hunger, disease, and privation. Further, we must press ahead in the name of the human adventure. Without experimentation and change our existence would be a dull business. We simply cannot stop while there are masses to feed and diseases to conquer, seas to explore and heavens to survey.

Samuel C. Florman, *The Existential Pleasures of Engineering*, 1994

In the spirit of Seneca's "All art mimicks nature," syncopating neurogenesis to more patterns than Earth spawns at that preliminary lifestage has befallen *Homo sapiens* as automatically as fused sand became its glass for correcting imperfect vision, letting light indoors, and enclosing miniature suns . . . so twigs form birdnests or trees beaverdams. A similar admonition by Wordsworth--"Let nature be your teacher"-- continues to instruct us: Our native domain is now fashioned from steel and microchip no differently than it once employed skin, straw, stone, or clay. Those who would take up arms against what might be fashionably found unnatural forget swords scarcely sprout from iron deposits: Hirsute as polyester, neoLuddites express their antiscientific displeasure over the telephone--having been irked by information obtained from television, radio, or newsprint, while eating meals hardly cooked on wood stoves and drinking refrigerated beverages in an environment flooded with artificial light, warmed electrically, its

117

air depollenized, *et cetera.* Like Vitruvius, Daniel Dennett nicely undermines the dichotomy between nature and its multifarious products--including genetically engineered variants or, by extension, artifacts allowing such creativity . . . even angelic denizens derived from novel technology (his caveat openly invites this book's subject):

> No man is an island, John Donne proclaims, and Charles Darwin adds that neither is any clam or tulip--every *possible* living thing is connected to all other living things. Notice that this doctrine rules *in* whatever marvels technology can produce in the future, provided . . . that technologies, and their tools and methods, are firmly located on the Tree of Life . . . .
>
> The truly wise engineer works not *contra naturam* but *secundum naturam.*

Samuel Florman, whose exhortative quote prefaces this chapter, would presumably agree; in Gregory Stock's *Metaman,* the same, recalling Herbert Spencer a century before: "Civilization is not an intrusion into the natural realm, but a harmonious extension of it."

Our motive could not be more instinctual--in lieu of inherent meaning, a conspiring universe equips us with the curiosity to fashion purpose; experiments stem from generic discontent impacting each of us, therefore illuminated consciousness will seek variety to the soporific rule. If momentarily satisfied, a mind which matters to itself--the ultimate judge--must question that conscience which can leave another's pain unaddressed, nor is provisional wisdom an excuse for not ever quickening the quest after unconditional love . . . both its reception and rendering.

Prenatal stimulation merely recasts in contemporary format venerable music revering a new member of the human tribe; before the healthcare community started regarding pregnancy as a problematic condition, gravid mothers danced to chants or drumbeats indelibly touching their unborn babies--which is the reason postnatal infants fix an avid ear near a parent's heart, and quiet at being rocked with that motion intimately recalling gestational sway. By simply supplementing through technology this essential influence--a direct descendant of luckily redundant and therefore imprintable cardiation--an ancient clue to multifactorial capacity has been furthered with highly efficacious lifespan repercussions.

If we no longer shy from vaccinating where the outdated norm would have vacated responsibility for a host organism, as childless partners finally conceive their dream by pipette, when the future is construed through ideas in blueprint and cybertext, these initially alien yet now quite accepted acts are proving not our secondary but primary character--yesterday's magic become banal, the momentary fear already fading while tomorrow is known faster than imagination can travel. Truly, inveterate tinkering describes this planet's most honorable craft, an occupation entirely fit for *Homo faber*, that creature lately reinventing its own character. Against fetal advantaging alarmists may raise the eugenics specter (or its forerunner, stirpiculture), what from principled animal breeding went grotesquely awry under racist pogroms inflamed by one prejudice or another, beyond sane description, devolving to a barbarous pseudoscience. Prebirth enrichment discriminates against no one--and through creative commerce even the poorest can be accommodated. Luther Burbank's analogizing from lifelong plant experiments to us transcends his chauvinisms, reflecting the intent which care alone confers:

> I may only refer to that mysterious prenatal period, and say that even here we should begin our work, throwing around the mothers of the race every possible loving, helpful, and ennobling influence; for in the doubly sacred time before the birth of a child lies, far more than we can possibly know, the hope of the future of this ideal race which is coming upon this earth if we and our descendants will it so to be.

With an incipient millennium to freshen perspective, let us frankly admit that humans pursue pervasive intervention merely as continuance of nature selecting for survival--biology and culture each replicate with net advancements, the sole difference being which is more efficient.

This is not to say dangers seldom threaten our more adventurous meddling: Bioengineers have delivered wonders and promise further, yet who decides which genetic feature is modified? Would humor or tenderness be excised for a perverse end? However much agricultural cloning portends for developing country food supplies (while new challenges arise from resulting perturbations in the global ecosystem), any duplication or gross redesign among humans not only teases but terrifies the imagination. As Gina Maranto warns in *Quest for Perfection*, we should be rightly frightened if endearing traits like whimsy or bathos fall before the microscopic blade. Opposing any specific intrusion, prenatal enrichment administered by curricularizing a fundamental rhythmicity frequents through broadest sonic strokes *all* faculties in concert with our double helix inheritance--no single attribute can be isolated for alteration; talents less spectacular in the bloodline, or those entirely new, are primed to blossom, though not upon precise demand: The *whole* self benefits. Even now, animal trials indicate success in inducing postnatal brain cell growth to offset damaged tissue--research which holds great potential for humans--and not far removed DNA manipulation or targeted magnetic pulses (these already at the experimental stage) may retard fetal apoptosis, perhaps in translation beyond the individual, bestowing yet further benefits than what my efforts produced. But until that portentous day, the approach presented here is both safe and sure.

Once I witnessed the manifold virtues of in utero rescue from a lately ineffective standard--first mentally, then on paper, next in children manifesting achievements never before constant, and at last borne out by researchers sifting data from thousands of gifted instances--commercialization was the only prudent decision science could entertain, just as other crash projects race to stem emergencies. Applying George Basalla's historical perspective from *The Evolution of Technology*, in an environment where capital is the mass conversion of idea to

120

action, marketing the system became a timely virtue: "If evolutionary change is to occur, then novelty must find a way to assert itself in the midst of the continuous."

To have witheld this opportune option from whichever baby possessed an enlightened supporter--be they parent, other relative, friend, or physician--would have been commiting the worst immorality . . . failing the fetal plea, ignoring those normative victims of a biologic morphology past its prime. In the cultural struggle for elevating achievement, victory emerged: Doomed genetically, upon departing its birthplace the mortal protobrain nigh extinct, our provoked but providential mind has conceived a cure--the imprintable preventive cued by natural selection; any resort short of merciful stewardship, salvaging lapsed neurology, perpetrates an acute unconscionability, constituting in the endless battle for environmental betterment a flagrant failure. The wrestling ethic between our kind's outdated dynamic and human developmental engineering has been genuinely juxtaposed.

Ego, at its cleverest where claiming institutionalized authority, gives no more ground than granite anticipates an earthquake; behind expected quibbles--dispelled once uninformed opinion is countered by durable data--hardcore opponents of this prebirth solution typically fail to recognize a species in crisis while their invested inhibition perpetuates that mass psychosis identified by Freud (most notably in his final testament, *Civilization and Its Discontents*). A prevailing *déformation professionnelle* is incisively described by C. Owen Paepke in *The Evolution of Progress*:

> . . . the sheer breadth of progress defeats the efforts of specialists to understand it. Explaining the world within the accepted framework of their specialties is the raison d'être of experts . . . . The canons of each discipline impose a straightjacket on its practitioners and virtually compel a hypertrophic elaboration of increasingly sterile premise. Only an amateur, who can search with a floodlight rather than a laser beam, has any hope of discovering phenomena that spread across a vast intellectual, historical, and factual

121

terrain. Seminal works of Marshall McLuhan, Jane Jacobs, and Rachel Carson were conspicuous demonstrations of the strength of the generalist's perspective. The narrow and deep credentials that now dominate the intellectual landscape are a serious if not fatal impediment to any understanding of progress.

Alternatively, extrapolation of the Hippocratic oath (where "first do no harm" presumes the common innocuous, collective dysfunction unobserved or ignored)--motivating physicians not otherwise responsible to administer more than restoration of an always relative status quo--would invoke proactive participation in elevating evolution's implicate vector at the medical level, a role model for *every* occupation and behavior. Isolated knowledge remains effete, and only its muscular movement justifies learning; particularly when crisis nears, tested ethics must act aggressively rather than mock that intelligence which promotes vigorous vision. Dedicated dilettantism (expertise at a discount price, since no matter the professional precedent anyone encountering newness is a novice) by demand, the day for observation alone--from specialists or parents--is over.

As this metamorphic mission continues, overhauling our inception, relevant advances in fetal brain science take place with inspiring frequency: A quite disguised blessing, their problematic source has become the putative remedy for Down syndrome, autism, certain forms of schizophrenia, and numerous mental disorders (where neurons are generally smaller, developing shorter branches), while a prenatal factor is now proposed even if genetic or postbirth components pertain; certain degenerative diseases associated with aging--Alzheimer's and Parkinson's as examples--might also be confirmed partly gestational in origin. These afflictions are therefore theoretically susceptible to control by neurogenetic enrichment. Except when parents with a prediagnosed Down's fetus opted for BabyPlus as an offsetting influence (preliminarily favorable in numerous instances), during longterm trials of those sonically enfranchised before birth, none of the disablities indicated above--nor any other--has ever appeared.

122

A few tangential topics bear noting. Extreme vulnerability on the one hand and plasticity on the other so mark our formative months that their mixture may be responsible for the rare phenomenon called savantism, where prodigious mathematical, musical, or artistic ability appears in usually autistic individuals; I proposed its source as prenatal to psychiatrist Darold Treffert-- clinical advisor for the popular film portraying this condition, *Rain Man*--who subsequently reported the possibility in his 1989 book, *Extraordinary People.*

Another suggestion for our widest developmental window: Current hospital use of recorded children's melodies to stimulate premature infants through miniature headphones may not just boost oxygen in the blood and regularize cardiac rates along with breathing, it could replace neurogenetic sustenance from an interrupted in utero maternal heartbeat--perhaps advantaging the still formative protobrain were the sonic content progressively sequenced; incubator redesign critically awaits this innovation.

Lately, thicker placentas have been found surrounding newborns who experienced BabyPlus, which could indicate responsive movement by the unborn child in turn massaging the womb wall, sonic vibration affecting cellular growth, or hormone concentration as a maternal placebo impact. Investigation of our severest deficits or best assets more and more couples genetics with earliest receptivity to environmental cause, in many ways diminishing the traditional dominance inheritance plays. Reiterating the vital linkage: If richer protobrain experience bequeaths increased physical resistance to insult, the net cortical loss at birth will minimally rather than importantly impair the infant, in turn rectifying negative preconception or gestational influences from parents who inadvertantly inflict biochemical or stressful scarring.

Moreover, it is not outside reason--from idiosyncratic though partially curricularized activities involving sound, undertaken during pregnancies in the 1970s (antedating the portable audiocassette player), their recipients now well past adolescence --that lifetime dependencies upon alcohol, tobacco, mood- altering drugs, and psychological states like compulsion, obsession, or control, may be modified by inducing at the earliest

123

moment our proclivity for order . . . establishing patterns that several mainstream studies have found to expand reasoning powers, afford emotional stability, and strengthen the young self-image so important for assisting others despite the raging vagaries of a materialistic age.

An alternative of merit concerning the abortion issue has also surfaced: Whether from rape, incest, diagnosis of extreme prenatal deficit, or private decision a woman does not wish pregnancy, formerly her choices were restricted to termination, adoption, or raising an unwanted child. In contrast, daily sonic stimulation could serve as an active countermeasure to the perhaps undesired circumstances precipitating conception, or discovery of a severely jeapordized fetus; that growing bond between parent and baby engaged by the interactivity of first communication slowly distances negative considerations, therefore the life inside acquires durable identity and often its name. Such a personalizing process raises vital options: The decision to abort can be offset either by more intimate awareness of the developing offspring, an emotional attachment assuring the neonate is maternally retained--as a now accepted and gifted family member--or offered for adoption knowing its chances of achieving long-term success are enormously enlarged. Since this aspect touches upon moral and demographic matters, at times I have been asked to furnish fetal enrichment information for religious and governmental bodies.

On a related subject, the implications of fetal enrichment upon the global population explosion are equally profound. Following a 1994 United Nations conference in Cairo where 180 countries pledged to moderate the projected world doubling rate, peaking at about ten billion by 2050, by offering health and contraceptive information to mothers, that consensus has not surprisingly degenerated into partisan disputes--while our numbers have now surpassed six billion. However, women who give birth to prenatally primed offspring can see what their additional resourcefulness means to the family dynamic, whether greater child wellbeing, enhanced interpersonal rewards, or higher income . . . and these assets in one individual can weigh against bearing many babies of lesser potential. Particularly among developing regions where human concentration is most dense, parents thus empowered also have with this technology a lever to massively move not just immediate communities but the world toward unanticipated betterment. That halcyon scenario deserves lowest cost products, be they born of entrepreneurial ingenuity, private patronage, or institutional largess.

Yet if the ethics of commercial application may be tangibly argued, consider those demonstrably empathic skills imparted to an upcoming generation--in starkest contrast with that emotional woodenness accompanying mental deficit, the sociopath's indifference. When criticism brands as spurious the causes behind children inclined to share rather than hoard, assist instead of avoid, perhaps scrutiny might turn upon the questioner's motives: *Who* would be upset when youths of any race or economic status--not just due to superlative intelligence but unremitting kindness--are accepted by prestigious academic institutions on full scholarship, reliably outperform in the workplace, as well as make better citizens, partners, and parents? What real threat is intellect inflected with charm even while surpassing authority's attainments?

The underlying problem impugns human definition: Should our essence remain conveniently static (which in macroscopic practice it never has) or openly evolve; and, if suppressed by inertia from a shopworn paradigm, whose obstructionist interests are at stake? Pertinent to these transformative times and their furtherance as described here, John Maddox, a former *Nature* editor, distills the issue:

> The general distrust of science has other and more primitive roots. To the extent that science and its applications bring improvements in our lot, they also imply change, and change is never welcome for its own sake.

Public reluctance to alter any status quo--sometimes even the most deprived conditions--figures as a dominant feature of ecological niche security, interim though an organism's residence may be; for an evolutionary dynamic, the ironic good fortune incumbent in resistance to alteration is that the inevitable

defects deriving therefrom precipitate the very transition feared
. . . with a resulting fresh perspective only its few precursors
anticipated.

This is why large quantities of BabyPlus have been donated
to needy nations, for averting future crises and exercising
contributor conscience: Salvation starts by seeding generic
beneficence, with gains attending the giver in addition to the
recipient.   If over an ethical expanse the technology renders
indigenous that unconstrained altruism previously embodied
among the rarest exemplars, instead of the material reciprocity
meager neurology seeks, quite another reward surfaces: Spiritual
leaders, heroes, and idealists are frequently forced to sacrifice
their lives (what might be termed *martyrdom equity*) rather than
compromise principles because virtuous conviction stands in
vivid contrast with consensus, which confuses *thing* with
thought, no incarnate necessity but a force outside physical
existence--the message transcends its medium.   Sociobiologists
point to a moral high ground above the classic test of Prisoner's
Dilemma as Tit for Tat (see Robert Trivers, *Social Evolution*),
but an even greater behavioral elegance is *Winner Gives All*--
history most recalls and civilization has advanced fastest from
personages whose absence instructs more than any other
presence, having bypassed through cultural selection contenders
whose ideas or deeds failed to survive.

The ultimate morality of prenatal stimulation resides in its
usage: parents who care enough to risk the loss of a
comparatively partial past, and insure for their genetic successors
the fullest outcome; if so paradoxical an affection produces
discomfort among those content with or hiding from the human
present, then it surely addresses urgent issues.

Chapter Twelve--*Everyone's World*

A child is love itself.

Milan Kundera, *Immortality*, 1990

Each expectant parent should understand what neurogenesis mandates: As detailed in Chapter Five, a majority of their unborn baby's brain shall die before birth, an endemic condition premodern ages had to accept but, facing unprecedented challenges yet armed with better science, we do not; children restricted by the former standard will be condemned to become prematurely passé, the castaways of their generation. With this revised knowledge--which today includes one special practice responsible parenthood requires and research supplies--either procreation is taken more seriously than in any previous period or an infant will be evolutionarily sidetracked. Though political perspective has been proverbially suspect, in her book, *It Takes a Village and Other Lessons Children Teach Us*, Hillary Rodham Clinton (an impassioned proponent of improving prenatal care, and the force behind a 1997 White House symposium on early learning's link to neural growth) properly grieves: ". . . we are not paying enough attention to what ought to be our highest priority: educating and empowering people to be the best parents possible." A superlative standard for childbearing and rearing defines timeliness: That boldest niche now embracing us crucially demands adaptation by those who manufactured much of it; since they are cast from an obsolete mold, their only viable choice is bettering the template--for which curricularized sonic stimulation of the fetus may be claimed a cultural enhancer.

No mentally healthy individual considering their posterity can ignore the ominous implications inherent in Earth's demographic gradient; its near 90-degree upswing should burn like Hawthorne's scarlet letter or the harrowed engraving Kafka envisioned for prisoners in his penal colony--this more than any other postnatal factor will sorely shape our new century. The

127

awesome specters of overpopulation and nightmare weaponry are materializing with a maniacal vehemence demanding attention from couples who wish their reproductive act to have meaning, that outcome ideally endowed for resolving titanic crises brought on by less than enfranchised billions. Should even mention of the onrushing cataclysm seem pitiless, politically reprehensible, an offense to decorum (at least among developed countries), consider in physically grave terms that direst rival if we do not practice joint ethical judgement: What does tomorrow's child deserve--the minimal biologic resources serving yesterday or the technological gift an enlightened future has bequeathed in wrapt anticipation? Mindful of the grimmest inklings, counterweight to utopian sentiment, our impending dilemmas may drive extraterrestrial migration but they also symptomatize an archaically circumscribed human nature, as diagnosed by Susan Oyama:

> We have tried to educate and aid the poor, and the poor are still with us. We have claimed our legacy as lords of the earth, and the earth is disintegrating around us. We have tried to construct an egalitarian state, but gender, class and ethnic boundaries still vex us. We "rehabilitate" criminals, and they victimize us again. We modernize underdeveloped nations, and they revile us. We construct a therapeutic ethic of individualistic freedom and fulfillment and find ourselves adrift in an ever more sophisticated wasteland. We manipulate the atom's nucleus, and it is threatening to annihilate us. Even our genealogies confound us: we claim the peaceloving chimpanzees as our nearest relatives and they subvert our moral phylogeny by killing each other.

Need another generation retrace its forebear's problematic path-- now strewn with boulders bigger than planets--or does direction spy interstitial favorability, a qualitative aperture through which one importunate species might squeeze and an expansive successor emerge? The disadvantaged fetus can hardly be faulted for their fate, since no newborn is held accountable if indifference or indecision deprives its life of a hitherto unavailable yet attractive avenue; but when beginning

128

consciousness becomes attended by care that rises above the commonly circumspect, then praise shall not cease: Abler answers from one assist all . . . an education the cosmos must applaud because as though by intent, despite apocalyptic threats en route, through Job's testing writ global it allows us a loving lesson--one we are in turn disseminating past any physical or mental perimeter.

Our paramount appeal impinges and will not go away: If a parent chooses against prenatal stimulation, they can be assured an unstoppable upwelling of babies merits contrarily--superlative competition fostered by the complex and crowded world already threatening even projected limits. But for those who wish to participate in the positive alteration of Earth's otherwise unassisted destiny, there has arisen an intimately rewarding option whose origin is the womb and contribution a lasting marriage with the veritable universe. Of the fetuses pending at present five births every second, each silently cries for that chance; as ranks of the rescued quickly replicate, soon not one should endure disappointment. A Keatsian reborrowing, which pertinently touched Robert Kaplan:

> And other spirits . . . are standing apart
> Upon the forehead of the age to come;
> These, these will give the world another heart,
> And other pulses. Hear ye not the hum
> Of mighty workings?--
> Listen awhile ye nations, and be dumb.

When the most sobering act is creation of life, then let its mortal issue represent the highest art and science our escape from yesterday affords; this book has aimed to place the task in a context of evolutionary pressure invoking positive cultural response, favorably tipping that breathless contest H. G. Wells identified: "Human history becomes more and more a race between education and catastrophe," politically brought current with Louis Halle's *The Elements of World Order*. Since authors--like lawyers, politicians, priests--must for credibility abide by their words, despite attempting to recant the line in his foreboding poem, "September 1, 1939," W. H. Auden was

129

inescapably emphatic, reifying the Christian essence: "We must love one another or die."

Because each generation in time faces upstart descendants, this instance merely reflects an added degree--but for once unthreatened by the younger perspective: It can ably ease the passage, more substantial yet less traumatic than ever before. If an ancillary reward from raising children is to gain personal perspective, learning firsthand what one's own mother or father experienced at a comparable age, through the genetically selected--their derivative character engaging life more in parallel with parental history than another--the chance to relive one's growth saga from hindsight increases when an offspring augments opportunity by way of a deeper bond.

Consider how Neandertals coexisted less cohabiting[1] with their eventual successors, Cro-Magnons: They seem to have lacked that retrospectively apt talent required for remaining successful players on the unfolding consciousness field. Although we do not know the precise explanation why this early neighbor (or now redated Java man) was marginalized to extinction, supplanted by a subtle superiority grown stark, the cautionary cause looms once again: *Change requires change*, and whoever cannot or will not remains unchanged--the forensic definition of death. When astronomer Eric Chaisson posits fixity as contravening life, he recalls Heraclitus no more than Damocles . . . whose sword hangs directly over us, both Draconian and Darwinian.

A terminal existence, meaning's absence, stands rebuked only through vivacious benevolence, scruples manifest in sensitivity, affection, sacrifice, care--the last word of Friedrich von Hügel, and an axiom pursued with psychoanalytic aplomb by Norman O. Brown; all slips or omissions admitted, our checkered record tells but one tale, collectively bittersweet:

---

[1] While a 1998 find of 25,000-year-old remains in Portugal may upon further testing show hybridization, perhaps Neandertal man was perceived as inferior despite possibly capable of speech, and, toward the end, producing superior tools, Pecksniffian segregation in effect; Loren Rieseberg's genetics experiments suggest emergent barriers that permit the optimal species certain exclusivities.

"Civilization traces merely the long process of learning to be kind,"[2] thereby seeking resonance with Verdi's affectionate universe--"Love is the cosmic constant." In upgrading the minimally reciprocal golden rule toward an empathic principle, the fetally optimized can advance where defensive predecessors fled: *Aggrandize that good engendered in the self.* John David Garcia also posits our goal of maximum urgency, applied individually and in toto: "The prime ethic of life is *each person must do his best to expand total awareness.*"

So, to arms, and those but embracing, in this test of neural mettle our war cry sprung from confirmed conscience: *We shall overcome ourselves.* The contest looms clearer than guilt outgrown; hearken to anthropological prognosticator, Jennifer James:

> Today, we stand in a vortex of technological, economic, demographic and cultural change. Are we to deny it, resist it, or accept the fact that we, too, must change?
>
> I believe that our current assignment is evolutionary, nothing less than the remaking of man and woman into a more civilized form than our ancestors. We must do it not within an extended family in a forest or on a vast savanna, but within what is becoming the human family in a global village.
>
> We cannot go backward; we cannot stand still. This is a personal journey, and we must *will* the direction.
>
> You can teach your mind to adapt to change, just as our bodies adapted to change through biological evolution. We must teach our children to increase their intelligence, to cooperate, to think in new ways. It is a tough assignment, but one that we must make a commitment to if we are to prosper in the years ahead.
>
> The key is the ability to "think in the future tense."

---

2 Revisionist doubters should read Lawrence Keeley's *War Before Civilization: The Myth of the Peaceful Savage*, Shepard Krech's *The Ecological Indian: Myth and History*, or Rod Preece's *Animals and Nature: Cultural Myths, Cultural Realities.*

These words reverberate with a familiar refrain; in speaking of Aldous Huxley's "perennial philosophy"--while referencing an archetypal flux and fidelity T. S. Eliot or Joseph Campbell would dearly recognize--Erich Jantsch notes:

> . . . human life is sharing integrally in a greater order of process, that it is an aspect as well as an *agent* of universal evolution. The fear of losing static security in a given structure and of being swept along by an unpredictable stream thus becomes transformed into *hope*--the hope associated with *life*, with the dynamic notions of continuity and transformability, of being embedded in a purpose and meaning transcending ourselves and the lives of our transitory systems, the hope inherent in the nondualistic experience of *being* the stream.

George A. Seielstad, *At the Heart of the Web*, elevates this evolutionary mechanism to a cultural mandate: "We inherit an obligation to permit life's progression to prosper."

Amplifying ancient capacities for social and natural interface that have now become distanced, the group formerly related by blood or biophilic ties seeks far larger kinship--first through new ideas, then realities grown less virtual--encouraging farflung intimacy, no longer self-centered but communally committed . . . even unto the stars whose very stuff comprises us. Bridging spans which ever shrink from infinity to footsteps are progeny, their principal role prophesied through Oswald Spengler's organic historicism, "Connecting yesterday and tomorrow is the child," or Eugenio Montale's existential escape clause, "Our future lies in the hands of children." We transitional sponsors must learn to give way with grace--what previous generations called the soul or character, and today passes as consciousness; that most genuine of generosites, gained over wise lifetimes, will become a triumphant legacy, one's personal departure from this little planet prelude to an inevitable homecoming awaited by the heavens like doting parents.

Afterword

To you yet unborn these, seeking you.

Walt Whitman, "Full of Life Now," 1859

Judicious readers reaching these final remarks should likely inhabit quite another place from the book's outset, and that locale can be recapitulated by a few key facts; mulled with diligence or idly, their order no fiat, they solicit catalysis-- ideally, further exploration--wherever cogent:

During gestation a developmental window opens through which only certain yet necessary information may pass-- imprinting's unique focus.

Sound has been identified as the foremost prenatal sensory influence, particularly maternal heartbeat.

As detected by electroencephalography, auditory driving can govern the rate at which synapses fire, a measure of how well the brain processes experience.

Genetically programmed and almost total protobrain cell death coincides with the end of full-term pregnancy, concluding before fear commences shortly after birth.

Exceedingly different neuroanatomies of retardation and giftedness have been discovered--a direct connection between physiology and performance.

The progressive or iterated nature of learning is not a random collection of stimuli; because most sounds in the mother's environment reach every unborn child but unlike repetitive curricularized material adapted from her in utero

133

bloodpulse have no imprintable effect, as confirmed by comparative testing neither the complex patterns of music nor speech directed at the pregnant abdomen significantly enhance fetal or postnatal development.

Advent of the portable audiocassette player, electronic microchip, their prenatal application, and concurrent development of the digital sampling device permit the womb's precise sonic replication.

Multiple validations are demonstrating consistently elevated mental, social, and creative attributes for thousands of children from every economic milieu who experienced curricularized fetal sonic stimulation; this phenomenon suggests the human protobrain, by undergoing mitigation of cell death through a cultural process, is being durably enriched to pronounced individual and collective benefit.

The above tenets fashion an original landscape, entrance into which constitutes that perceptual birth required for "seeing with new eyes," Proust's vital observation; it is increasingly peopled by those of expansive mind and expressive heart.

They come--first as babies cradled by parents in cautious awe though clearly delighted with what their curious occupation during pregnancy has wrought, then children phoning nonstop, filling my postbox, modeming at warpspeed, all smiles before an entryway even now accessing a world the past would find idyllic; an unprecedented adulthood awaits them, perennial youths emboldened in vision and vigor for the bigger tasks our present shirks or precipitates.

Just as employers for not entirely the same reason have begun inquiring about these potential hirees, how to guage the genuine article, test ethical acidity, litmus a moral assay? After concocting countless student examinations--which, no less than presumption undone, provoke a reverse scrutiny--this former teacher synthesizes characterological measurement three ways,

134

so simplistically difficult, obvious as avoidance, damnable for directness.

First, one fiscal question:[1] *Should a fortune more than ever dreamed befall you, who or what gains?* (This same interrogative holds under opposite circumstance, weighing penurious philanthropy.) Another query, existentially acute but no altruistic progression: *Is your life worth sacrificing for a friend, any stranger, humanity, our planet, the future, an idea, some ideal?* Finally, explain both answers by presenting a plan: *Beyond why, how?*

All applicants for my wrapt attention pass muster--I have turned no empathic candidate away; each of their neurons knows beyond synaptic hesitation that true conservatism is radically liberal, the dissipating plenum artifactually reconstituted through consumptive immolation. William Irwin Thompson's *Coming into Being* sounds a perfect pitch:

> . . . this new planetary culture is not simply a reaction to our new technologies--be they aerospace, atomic, genetic, or electronic--but an expression of a spiritual evolution that is actually pulling out these new technologies. From this perspective, I see the Zeitgeist as serving as midwife to the birth of a new humanity.

Yet so transformative a matter has not been mine from choice alone: The force which brought forth an awakening like no other was forged through hands which often appeared unfamiliar--nothing metaphysical though strangely irresistible, as if manipulated by time itself (Herbert Spencer, "Progress…is not an accident, but a necessity…."); today their happiness is to shake those far more skilled, ones stretching infinitely past me, further than the personally fortuitous. With his usual lucid verve

---

[1] Where pragmatic philosophy must start--why Henry David Thoreau's opening chapter for *Walden*, "Economy," lists his operational costs, or Henry Miller commenced both *Tropic of Cancer* and *Capricorn* with a materially destitute but overflowing spreadsheet of individualistic principles.

Stuart Kauffman states my concluding sentiment, *The Origins of Order* deserving penultimacy:

> The greater mystery, after all, is not the answers that scientists contrive, but the questions they are driven to pose. Why? Why this question rather than another? Why this search, hope, despair, rather than another? Why this ill-lit, nil understood, hobo path? And why the outrageous confidence, born of no evidence, to tred it? I do not know. But I know that this sense is not rare. What a strange pleasure it is to seek . . . .
>
> Authors know that books are not easily written. This one has been no exception. Yet writing a scientific book can be like writing a novel. Ideas, like characters, once loose upon a page harbor their own lives, follow their own unsuspected paths, mature in unforeseen ways, and mingle with their own logic. If useful, they have progeny.

Our old niche closes, surprisingly narrow before this latest domain, less place than process--a river of ever influential dimension, expanding its banks, etching deeper the channel, an inspired bloodline formed by that confluence from now instinctively empathic families which over but one fecund generation shall cover the Earth with untold promise . . . waters rapidly rising to heal, help, and hurry us toward the receptive cosmic sea, birthplace immense as tomorrow.

Our flaws and evils are too frequent, but forgetting the young is worse. All else can wait--the child, not one instant. As we speak, bones, blood, and senses are first stirring. Children must never be told *later* . . . their very name is *now*.

Gabriela Mistral, *A Call for the Child*, 1948

Appendix--*Prenatal Enrichment Chronology*

Prehistory Gestation rituals include dancing to instrumental music; still observed in Polynesian, African, and Asian tribal practices involving the pregnant mother.

c. 500 BCE Confucius infers that the fetal environment can determine behavior.

c. 450 BCE Chinese culture formalizes special childbearing treatment, thereby acknowledging health, dietary, emotional, and stimulatory effects--including sound-- upon the fetus.

c. 400 BCE Plato asserts that vibration is the primary cosmic principle.

c. 350 BCE Prenatal receptivity to external factors surmised by Aristotle.

c. 400 The surgeon Susruta of India believes the unborn child begins seeking sensation late in the first trimester, its mind at work by five months.

c. 600 Talmudic writings reference fetal awareness.

c. 1000 Japan adapts Chinese prebirth arts to its society, institutionalizing their practice as *taikyo*; over time, this focus shifts from superstitious precautions to a theistic and then imperial rationale, by the 20th century amalgamated with an overtly educational approach.

1690 *An Essay Concerning Human Understanding*, by the British philosopher, John Locke, contains the presumption that a fetus is capable of thought, and its ideas can be influenced from outside the womb.

1881 William Preyer, in *The Mind of the Child*, claims cerebral functions are initiated before birth.

c. 1890 As the Quing dynasty of China is forming a republic, the civic expectations for progeny advance ancient fetal intervention techniques, centering upon utopian aims.

1924 Albrecht Peiper, a Leipzig University pediatrician, visually confirms prenatal response to outside stimuli by observing distension from kicking in the maternal abdomen after an automobile horn is sounded.

1920s-50s Increasing evidence of second-trimester audition and multisensory fetal reaction to the maternal environment, with in utero learning suggested by psychologist David Spelt; psychologist Donald Hebb, McGill University, Montreal, posits a neurogenetic hypothesis that early enrichment produces physiological changes in the brain which promote reasoning abilities.

1960s New York psychologist, Lee Salk, conducts investigations of prenatal imprinting from the mother's blood surging past the placenta, identifying various permanent behavioral indicators; neuroanatomist Marian Diamond at the University of California, Berkeley, begins three decades of research which reveal stimulating maternal environments alter brain physiology in rat offspring, and increase their learning skills; auditory driving discovered--Andrew Neher shows how sonic patterns can influence alpha rhythm in the brain.

1962 Ashley Montagu's *Prenatal Influences* summarizes the expanding information about fetal life.

1970s-80s Technology provides more accurate monitoring of gestational processes, including photographic images which enhance public perceptions of the unborn child.

1971   Prenatal psychology commences as a scientific discipline with the Vienna founding of its first professional organization, another group beginning in Toronto a decade after.

1980   Introduction of the portable audiocassette player, the Sony Walkman; parents worldwide start applying headphones to the maternal abdomen, producing fetal movement and claims for infant benefits.

1980s   Anthony DeCasper, a University of North Carolina psychologist, finds that newborns prefer speech heard before birth, favoring the maternal voice; at the Eastman School of Music in Rochester, New York, Donald Shetler has pregnant students play recorded classical music to the womb through adjacent headsets, with their children demonstrating early musical skills.

1981   In *The Secret Life of the Unborn Child*, Toronto psychiatrist Thomas Verny and co-writer John Kelly compile anecdotes of assorted fetal effects upon later life.

1982   Media reports about Americans Joseph and Jitsuko Susedik having stimulated with mixed means their four daughters before birth and throughout childhood during the prior decade, all girls demonstrating giftedness; Brent Logan proposes curricularized variations of maternal in utero heartbeat sounds as a neurogenetic improvement, initiates comprehensive theoretical research, and invents the earliest prenatal enrichment technology.

1984   Upon learning from his patients about fetal responsiveness to abdominal touch, California obstetrician René Van de Carr develops a stimulation methodology of tactile manipulations paired with words describing these actions.

141

1986   Brent Logan presents prelearning theory before professional congresses, then inaugurates pilot studies to verify his contention; René Van de Carr publishes the first clinical evidence showing neonatal and infant assets from fetal intervention.

1987-88   The first babies experiencing in the womb an imprintable sonic progression under Brent Logan's projects are born; he begins a series of related articles in academic journals.

1989-90   Commercialization commences of prebirth enrichment technology created by Brent Logan, with 3000 children advantaged.

1990s   Numerous studies link the earliest sonic influences to youth and adult proficiency; Brent Logan designs second and third-generation prenatal enhancement products, with extensive donation of units to developing countries, benefitting more than 100,000 children from all living conditions. Various unsafe or ineffective devices enter the market.

2003   Publication of the first comprehensive resource on fetal enrichment--Brent Logan's *Learning Before Birth: Every Child Deserves Giftedness.*

Selected general references citing the author's prenatal enrichment research

Adderly, Brenda, and Gordon, Jay, *Brighter Baby: Boost Your Child's Intelligence, Health, and Happiness*, LifeLine/Regnery, Washington, D.C., 1999

Akhurst, Julie, Bach, babies, and brain power, *Junior*, London, May/June 1999

Alonso, Manuel, *Requiem Para Batman: Biografía Provisional de un Niño Prodigio*, Federico Domenech, Valencia, 1990

BabyPlus--a local user's view, *Northern Ireland Baby Magazine*, Belfast, March 1996

BabyPlus--the new ante-natal phenomenon? *Northern Ireland Baby Magazine*, Belfast, February 1996

BabyPlus device and mothers, *Tamil Nesan*, Kuala Lumpur, April 1996

BabyPlus device--education starts in the womb, *New Life Post*, Kuala Lumpur, April 1996

BabyPlus improves child intelligence, *Malaysia Nanban*, Kuala Lumpur, April 1996

BabyPlus inventor in Kuala Lumpur, *Utusan Malaysia*, Kuala Lumpur, March 1996

BabyPlus launched, *The Financial Express*, Madras, India, September 1996

Barber, Marsha, Better babies, CBC Television, Toronto, March 1990

Before baby's born, WFTV/ABC Television, Orlando, February 1990

Before birth, *Female*, Kuala Lumpur, May 1996

Begley, Sharon, Do you hear what I hear? *Newsweek*, Special Edition, How kids grow: coming into the world, Summer 1991

Benefits of prenatal stimulation touted, *The Malay Mail*, Kuala Lumpur, March 1996

Bondy, Natasha, Can you make a genius?, BBC Television, London, June 2001

Brainy babies, *Wellcome News Online*, The Wellcome Trust, London, Third Quarter 2000

Brent Logan, radio interview, BBC, London, December 1997, June 1998

Brent Logan, radio interview, CBC, Toronto, December 1997

Brent Logan, radio interview, NPR, Washington, D.C., December 1997

Brent Logan, television interview, Channel 4, London, January 1998

Brewer, Sarah, *Super Baby: Boost Your Baby's Potential from Conception to Year One*, Thorsons/HarperCollins, London, 1998

Brooks, Dana, BabyPlus--a gift for a lifetime, *Executive Woman*, London, February/March 1995

Brott, Armin, and Ash, Jennifer, *The Expectant Father: Facts, Tips, and Advice for Dads-to-Be*, New York, Abbeville, 1995, revised edition 2001

Brown, Lisa, Wonder babies, KCRA Television, Sacramento, November 1989, NBC/Lorimar Telepictures, Los Angeles, February 1990

Burbridge, David, Baby boom boom, *The Northern Echo*, Darlington, UK, March 1990

Can they hear what we hear? BabyPlus UK Limited, London, May 1995

Chambers, Dan, *Brave New Babies*, Broadcasting Support Services, London, 1994

Chew, Marjorie, A big plus for baby, *The Star*, Kuala Lumpur, September 1996

Chew, Marjorie, A head start with sonic stimulation, *The Star*, Kuala Lumpur, September 1996

Creating new millennium people, Korean Broadcasting System, Seoul, December 2000, January 2001

Culbertson, Katie, Unique product designed to give babies an edge, *Indianapolis Business Journal*, Indianapolis, August 2000

Das werdende Leben, Quarks & Co, WDR Television, Cologne, November 2001

Device to give unborn babies a head start, *New Straits Times*, Kuala Lumpur, March 1996

145

Duncan, Pippa, Listening and learning, *Baby Magazine*, London, April/May 1995

Einstein-machine makes baby smart, *Bildzeitung*, Hamburg, November 1994

Elwood, Patricia, Superbabies, CBS Television, New York, February 1996

Fajardo, Marie Anne I., Sonic stimulation for brighter babies? *The Manila Times*, Manila, April 1996

Fetal stimulator helps child development, *Berita Minggu*, Singapore, March 1996

Fetal teaching device, *Berita Harian*, Kuala Lumpur, March 1996

Future tense, Discovery Channel, Europe, June 2000

A genius child with BabyPlus, *Jelita*, Kuala Lumpur, May 1996

Gillespie, Elgy, America's unborn given a head start, *The London Times*, London, May 1989

Greene, Amanda, You are my sunshine, *Morning Star*, Wilmington, North Carolina, June 2001

Guten abend RTL, RTL Television, Cologne, forthcoming 2003

Hancock, Justine, Dig that music, baby, *The Independent*, London, March 1999

Hickman, David, producer and director, narrated by Miranda Richardson, Brave new babies, Equinox, Channel 4, London, November 1994; The Learning Channel, Bethesda, Maryland,

146

September 1995, December 1995, May 1996; Television Ontario, October 1995; Tevel Television, Israel, January 1996; Luxembourg Television, January 1996; Taiwan Television, January 1996; Singapore Television, March 1996; Channel 8, Israel, April 1998; Punt Z, Valencia, June 2002

Infant prodigies, *Prima*, London, April 1995

It's no baby talk, *WEEKENDeast*, Singapore, March 1996

Jarrett, Lisa, Taikyo--an ancient practice for the new millennium, *Indy's Child*, Indianapolis, July 1999

Jarrett, Lisa, Your baby's first teacher, *Pregnancy*, Atlanta, August/September 2000

Jones, Frank, Mother's heart music helps create superbabies, *Toronto Star,* Toronto, August 1989

Kam, Patsy, A new generation of geniuses, *The Star*, Kuala Lumpur, April 1996

Kam, Patsy, Making smart babies, *The Star*, Kuala Lumpur, April 1996

Landsman, Roberta, It's never too soon, *News-Chronicle*, Thousand Oaks, California, April 1990

Learning before birth, *The Sunday Republican,* Springfield, Massachusetts, May 1990

Learning before birth, *Wanita*, Kuala Lumpur, June 1996

L'école des foetus, *Le Nouvel Observateur,* Paris, April 1991

Lewis, Abigail, The Prelearning Program, *Whole Life Times*, April 1990

Logan, Brent, *Enigmata: A Prehistoric Fiction*, 1stBooks Library, Bloomington, Indiana, forthcoming.

Lundin, Diana, Learning before birth, *The New York Times*, April 1990

Making better babies, *New Woman*, Sydney, Australia, August 1990

Manlogon-Victoriano, Melanie, Dr. Mom trains babies inside the womb, *Woman Today*, Manila, October 1997

Manlogon-Victoriano, Melanie, Teaching babies with cardiac curriculum, *Woman's Home Companion*, Manila, September 1997

Marlowe, Kimberly, Beats for babies, *Journal American,* Bellevue, Washington, April 1990

Mason, Janet, How my baby joined the beat generation, *The Independent*, London, May 1995

Masuch, Denise, Intellectual development in the womb, World of Wonder, Prosieben Television, Munich, forthcoming 2003

Merewood, Anne, Pregnant with promise, *Vogue,* London, December 1990

Mitchell, Emily, Look who's listening too, *Time*, September 1991

Mitford, Jessica, The American way of birth, BBC Television, London, February 1993

Mitford, Jessica, *The American Way of Birth*, Dutton, New York, 1992

Morris, Gabrielle, Born genius? *Today*, London, November 1994

Neeraja, R., Sonic stimulus for brighter babies, *The Hindu*, Madras, India, September 1996

Noor, Halina, Teaching the fetus while in the womb, *Keluarga*, Kuala Lumpur, June 1996

Palmer, Jill, Is the superchild only a heartbeat away? *Daily Mirror*, London, November 1994

Porter, Mark, *Radio Times*, London, November 1994

Prenatal awareness is a heartbeat away, *Daily News*, Los Angeles, April 1990

The prenatal revolution: listening and learning with BabyPlus, *You & Your Baby*, London, May 1996

Prenatal sonic stimulation, Fox Television, New York, April 1997

Ridgway, Roy, *Caring for Your Unborn Child*, Harper & Row, San Francisco, 1991, Thorsons, Wellingborough, Northamptonshire, 1990

Shakeshaft, Lucy, Could wearing this device on your waist make your unborn child more intelligent? *Daily Mail*, London, November 1997

Shepherd, Rose, Listen with mother, *Daily Telegraph*, London, November 1997

Siegrist, J. C., El poder de la música, *Crecer Feliz*, Madrid, February 1992

Siegrist, J. C., Métodos que aumentan inteligencia, *Crecer Feliz*, Madrid, November 1993

Smith, Lee, A sound education, *The Sacramento Bee*, Sacramento, May 1990

Soria, Lorenzo, Le nuove frontiere, *L'Espresso*, Rome, September 1989

Starr, Penny, Baby's belly belt, *The Sun,* Las Vegas, May 1990

Stress affects the child in the womb, *The Star*, Kuala Lumpur, Malaysia, April 1996

Sullivan, Jane, Whizz kids, *The Guardian*, Manchester, UK, April 1990

The superpowers of babies, Japan Television, Tokyo, July 1992

Teaching a child while in the womb, *Berita Minggu*, Singapore, March 1996

Things to come, London Television/Independent Communications Associates, London, September 1990

Toms, Debbie, Boost your baby's IQ, *Daily Express*, London, November 1994

Treffert, Darold A., *Extraordinary People: Understanding "Idiot Savants,"* Harper & Row, New York, 1989

Tricaud, Jean-Marie, L'école des foetus, Zone Interdite, Métropole Télévision, Channel 6, Paris, November 1991, May 2000

Un apparecchio per avere un figlio intelligente, *Tirreno*, Livorno, Italy, March 1995

Unborn babies receive high-tech learning, *The Salisbury Post*, Salisbury, North Carolina, May 1990

Updates in prenatal stimulation, *Today's Parents,* Singapore, April 1996

Vachata, Linda, Early start for baby, *The Arizona Republic*, Phoenix, March 1990

Vinsrygg, Gudrun, Laring for ufødte, *Kvinner og Klar*, Oslo, February 1990

Weintraub, Pamela, Preschool? *Omni*, August 1989

Westcott, Patsy, Life before birth, *Pregnancy & Birth*, London, May/June 1995

Yancer, Jodi, Babytapes bolster unborns' knowledge, *The Highline Times*, Burien, Washington, June 1990

Yoke, Lee Lim Bee, Your child's happiness is only a heartbeat away, *The Company Secretary*, Kuala Lumpur, May/June 1996

You can make your baby intelligent when it is in the womb, *Makkal Osai*, Kuala Lumpur, April 1996

Other selected general references

Ádám, György, translated by Takácsi-Nagy, K., *Perception, Consciousness, Memory: Reflections of a Biologist*, New York, Plenum, 1980

Aristotle, *De Generatione Animalium*, Oxford, Oxford University, 1982

Baker, Robin, *Sperm Wars: The Science of Sex*, New York, BasicBooks, 1996

Barkow, Jerome H., Cosmides, Leda, and Tooby, John, editors, *The Adapted Mind: Evolutionary Psychology and the Generation of Cultures*, New York, Oxford University, 1992

Bates, Elizabeth, and Elman, Jeffrey, Learning rediscovered, *Science*, December 1996

Begley, Sharon, Getting inside a teen brain, *Newsweek*, February 2000

Begley, Sharon, The IQ puzzle, *Newsweek*, May 1996

Begley, Sharon, Your child's brain, *Newsweek*, February 1996

Berman, Morris, *The Twilight of American Culture*, New York, Norton, 2000

Bickerton, Derek, *Language and Human Behavior*, Seattle, University of Washington, 1995

Blakeslee, Sandra, The mystery of music: how it works in the brain, *New York Times*, May 1995

Bower, Bruce, The birth of schizophrenia: a debilitating mental disorder may take root in the fetal brain, *Science News*, May 1993

Bower, Bruce, Criminal intellects: researchers look at why lawbreakers often brandish low IQs, *Science News*, April 1995

Bower, Bruce, IQ's evolutionary breakdown: intelligence may have more facets than testers realize, *Science News*, April 1995

Bower, Bruce, Prenatal problems linked to schizophrenia, *Science News*, July 2000

Bower, Bruce, Tots take rhythmic stock before talk, *Science News*, September, 1994

Brian, Denis, *Einstein: A Life*, New York, John Wiley, 1996

Brown, Norman O., *Life Against Death: The Psychoanalytic Meaning of History,* Middletown, Connecticut, Wesleyan University, 1959

Burbank, Luther, *The Training of the Human Plant*, New York, Century, 1909

Calvin, William, *How Brains Think: Evolving Intelligence, Then and Now*, New York, BasicBooks, 1996

Calvin, William, *The Cerebral Code: Thinking a Thought in the Mosaics of the Mind*, Cambridge, Massachusetts Institute of Technology, 1996

Capra, Fritjof, *The Web of Life: A New Scientific Understanding of Living Systems*, New York, Bantam Doubleday Dell, 1996

Chaisson, Eric, *The Life Era: Cosmic Selection and Conscious Evolution*, New York, Atlantic Monthly Press, 1987

Chamberlain, David B., *Babies Remember Birth*, Los Angeles, Tarcher, 1988

Changeux, Jean-Pierre, *Neuronal Man: The Biology of Mind*, translated by Garey, L., New York, Pantheon, 1985

Clark, William R., *Sex and the Origins of Death*, New York, Oxford University, 1996

Clinton, Hillary Rodham, *It Takes a Village and Other Lessons Children Teach Us*, New York, Simon & Schuster, 1996

Clynes, Manfred, editor, *Music, Mind, and Brain: The Neuropsychology of Music*, New York, Plenum, 1982

Dawkins, Richard, *The Selfish Gene*, London, Oxford University, 1976/1989

Dawson, Geraldine, and Fischer, Kurt W., *Human Behavior and the Developing Brain*, New York, Guilford, 1994

della Cava, Marco R., The race to raise a brainier baby, *USA Today*, June 2002

Dennett, Daniel C., *Consciousness Explained*, Boston, Little, Brown, 1991

Dennett, Daniel C., *Darwin's Dangerous Idea: Evolution and the Meanings of Life*, New York, Simon & Schuster, 1995

Desmond, Adrian, and Moore, James, *Darwin: The Life of a Tormented Evolutionist*, New York, Warner Books, 1991

Diamond, Marian Cleeves, *Enriching Heredity: The Impact of the Environment on the Anatomy of the Brain*, New York, The Free Press, 1988

Diamond, Marian, and Hopson, Janet, *Magic Trees of the Mind*, New York, Dutton, 1998

Dobzhansky, Theodosius, *Mankind Evolving,* New Haven, Connecticut, Yale University, 1962

Doolittle, W. Ford, Silence of the genes, *Scientific American*, September 1995

Duke, Richard C., Ojcius, David M., and Young, John Ding-E, Cell suicide in health and disease, *Scientific American*, December 1996

Edelman, Gerald M., *Bright Air, Brilliant Fire: On the Matter of Mind*, New York, BasicBooks, 1992

Edelman, Gerald M., *Neural Darwinism: The Theory of Neuronal Group Selection*, New York, BasicBooks, 1987

Ehrlich, Paul R., *Human Natures: Genes, Cultures, and the Human Prospect,* Washington, D.C., Shearwater Books, 2000

Florman, Samuel C., *The Existential Pleasures of Engineering*, New York, St. Martin's, 1976/1994

Florman, Samuel C., *The Introspective Engineer*, New York, St. Martin's, 1996

Fowles, John, *The Aristos: A Self-Portrait in Ideas,* Boston, Little, Brown, 1964/1970

Freeman, Walter J., The physiology of perception, *Scientific American*, February 1991

Freud, Sigmund, *Civilization and Its Discontents*, London, The Hogarth Press, 1930

Frith, Uta, Autism, *Scientific American*, June 1993

Garcia, John David, *Creative Transformation: A Practical Guide for Maximizing Creativity*, Eugene, Oregon, Noetic Press/Ardmore, Pennsylvania, Whitmore Publishing, 1991

Garcia, John David, *A General Theory of Evolution and Creativity: Mathematical Foundations*, Eugene, Oregon, Noetic Press, 1997

Garcia, John David, *The Moral Society: A Rational Alternative to Death*, New York, The Julian Press, 1971

Garcia, John David, *Political Ethics: An Alternative to Destructive Tyranny*, Eugene, Oregon, Noetic Press, 1997

Gardiner, Howard, *Leading Minds: An Anatomy of Leadership*, New York, BasicBooks, 1995

Gibbs, Nancy, The EQ factor, *Time*, October 1995

Glass, Leon, and Mackey, Michael, *From Clocks to Chaos: The Rhythms of Life*, Princeton, Princeton University, 1988

Glausiusz, Josie, Brain, heal thyself, *Discover*, August 1996

Glausiusz, Josie, Micro gets macro, *Discover*, November 1995

Glausiusz, Josie, The neural orchestra, *Discover*, September 1997

Goleman, Daniel, *Emotional Intelligence*, New York, Bantam Books, 1995

Goodwin, Brian, *How the Leopard Changed Its Spots: The Evolution of Complexity*, New York, Charles Scribner, 1994

Gottlieb, Gilbert, *Individual Development and Evolution: The Genesis of Novel Behavior*, New York, Oxford University, 1992

Griffin, Donald R., *Animal Minds*, Chicago, University of Chicago, 1992

Grobstein, Clifford, *Science and the Unborn: Choosing Human Futures*, New York, Basic Books, 1988

Gutin, Jo Ann C., A brain that talks, *Discover*, June 1996

Halle, Louis J., *The Elements of World Order: Essays on International Politics*, Lanham, Maryland, University Press of America, 1995

Halle, Louis J., A hopeful future for humankind, *Foreign Affairs*, Summer 1980

Halle, Louis J., *Out of Chaos*, Boston, Houghton Mifflin, 1977

Hass, Robert, *Twentieth Century Pleasures*, New York, Ecco Press, 1984

Henderson, Hazel, quoted in The bull in the garden, *Civilization*, April/May 1998

Highfield, Roger, and Carter, Paul, *The Private Lives of Albert Einstein*, New York, St. Martin's, 1993

Hofer, Myron, *The Roots of Human Behavior*, San Francisco, W. H. Freeman, 1981

Holland, John, *Adaptation in Natural and Artificial Systems,* Ann Arbor, University of Michigan, 1975

Horgan, John, It's all in the timing: neurons may be more punctual than had been supposed, *Scientific American,* August 1995

Huntington, Samuel P., *The Clash of Civilizations and the Remaking of World Order,* New York, Touchstone, 1997

Huxley, Aldous, *The Perennial Philosophy,* New York, Harper, 1945

Huxley, Julian S., *Evolution, The Modern Synthesis,* London, Allen & Unwin, 1942

Ibuka, Masaru, *Zero-Years-Old: Where Education Really Begins,* Tokyo, Goma-shobou, 1986

James, Jennifer, *Thinking in the Future Tense: Leadership Skills for a New Age,* New York, Simon & Schuster, 1996

Kalin, Ned H., The neurobiology of fear, *Scientific American,* May 1993

Kauffman, Stuart, *At Home in the Universe: The Search for the Laws of Self-Organization and Complexity,* New York, Oxford University, 1995

Keeley, Lawrence H., *War Before Civilization: The Myth of the Peaceful Savage,* New York, Oxford University, 1996

Kingwell, Mark, Fast forward: our high-speed chase to nowhere, *Harper's,* May 1998

Knight, Jonathan, Early learning, *New Scientist,* January 2000

Krech, Shepard, *The Ecological Indian: Myth and History*, New York, Norton, 1999

Kuhn, Thomas, *The Structure of Scientific Revolutions*, Chicago, University of Chicago, 1962

Laily, Noor, *The Child of Excellence*, Nury Institute of Family and Child Development, Kuala Lumpur, 1992

Lovejoy, Arthur O., *The Great Chain of Being: A Study of the History of an Idea*, New York, Harper & Row, 1936

Lovelock, James E., *Gaia: A New Look at Life on Earth*, London, Oxford University, 1979

Ludington-Hoe, Susan, and Golant, Susan K., *How to Have a Smarter Baby*, New York, Rawson Associates, 1985

Lynch, Aaron, *Thought Contagion: How Belief Spreads Through Society*, New York, BasicBooks, 1996

Maranto, Gina, *Quest for Perfection: The Drive to Breed Better Human Beings*, New York, Scribner, 1996

Maugh II, Thomas H., Brain size linked to risk of dementia, *Los Angeles Times*, July 1994

McAuliffe, Kathleen, Making of a mind, *Omni*, October 1985

Miller, James Grier, *Living Systems*, New York, McGraw-Hill, 1978

Montagu, M. G. Ashley, *Prenatal Influences*, Springfield, Illinois, Thomas, 1962

Moore, David S., *The Dependent Gene: The Fallacy of Nature vs. Nature*, New York, W. H. Freeman, 2002

Morgan, Elaine, *The Descent of the Child*, New York, Oxford University, 1995

Moss, Frank, and Wiesenfeld, Kurt, The benefits of background noise, *Scientific American*, August 1995

Mothers' enriched environment alters brains of unborn rats, *Brain-Mind Bulletin*, volume 12, 1987

Motluk, Alison, Grow your own, *New Scientist*, February 2000

Munson, Marty, Plugged-in preemies: tunes may help infants breathe better, *Prevention*, July 1995

Myers, David G., and Diener, Ed, The pursuit of happiness, *Scientific American*, May 1996

Nash, J. Madeleine, Fertile minds, *Time*, February 1997

Neisser, Ulric, *Cognitive Psychology,* New York, Appleton-Century-Crofts, 1967

Norris, Tim, Bach for the babies, *Times-Union*, Rochester, New York, March 1984

Nowak, Martin A., May, Robert M., and Sigmund, Karl, The arithmetics of mutual help, *Scientific American*, June 1995

Oliwenstein, Lori, Death and the microbe, *Discover*, September 1995

Ormiston, Gayle L., and Sassower, Raphael, *Narrative Experiments: The Discursive Authority of Science and Technology*, Minneapolis, University of Minnesota, 1989

Overbye, Dennis, *Einstein in Love: A Scientific Romance,* New York, Viking, 2000

Paepke, C. Owen, *The Evolution of Progress: The End of Economic Growth and the Beginning of Human Transformation,* New York, Random House, 1993

Pearce, Joseph Chilton, *Magical Child,* New York, Plume, 1992

Piaget, Jean, *Behavior and Evolution,* translated by Nicholson-Smith, D., New York, Random House, 1978

Poole, William, The first 9 months of school, *Hippocrates,* July/August 1987

Popper, Karl, *Objective Knowledge: An Evolutionary Approach,* London, Oxford University, 1972

Popper, Karl, and Eccles, John, *The Self and Its Brain,* London, Springer-Verlag, 1977

Preece, Rod, *Animals and Nature: Cultural Myths, Cultural Realities,* Vancouver, University of British Columbia, 1999

Preyer, William T., *The Mind of the Child: The Senses and the Will,* New York, Appleton, 1881

Purves, Dale, *Body and Brain: A Trophic Theory of Neural Connections,* Cambridge, Harvard University, 1988

Raff, Martin C., Death wish, *The Sciences,* July/August 1996

Ramón y Cajal, S., *Recollections of My Life,* translated by Cragie, E. Horne, Cambridge, Massachusetts Institute of Technology, 1937

Rauscher, Frances, Music and reasoning, *Teaching Music*, April 1995

Ridgway, Roy, *Preparing for Parenthood*, London, Penguin, 1990

Roberts, Marjory, Class before birth, *Psychology Today*, May 1987

Rosen, Mortimer G., and Rosen, Lynn, *Your Baby's Brain Before Birth*, New York, New American Library, 1975

Roush, Wade, New knockout mice point to molecular basis of memory, *Science*, January 1997

Russell, Peter, *The Global Brain: Speculations on the Evolutionary Leap to Planetary Consciousness*, Los Angeles, Tarcher, 1983

Schechter, Bruce, How the brain gets rhythm, *Science*, October 1996

Schwartz, Leni, *Bonding Before Birth*, Boston, Sigo Press, 1991

Seielstad, George A., *At the Heart of the Web: The Inevitable Genesis of Intelligent Life*, New York, Harcourt Brace Jovanovich, 1989

Shepherd, Gordon M., *The Synaptic Organization of the Brain*, London, Oxford University, 1990

Shreeve, James, Music of the hemispheres, *Discover*, October 1996

Siefer, Werner, and Miltner, Frank, Gehirinforschung nervenkitzel, *Focus*, February 1997

Simpson, George Gaylord, *Tempo and Mode in Evolution*, New York, Columbia University Press, 1944/1984

Skinner, B. F., *Science and Human Behavior*, New York, Macmillan, 1953

Spencer, Herbert, *Social Statics*, New York, Appleton, 1883

Spengler, Oswald, *The Decline of the West*, New York, Knopf, 1926, 1928

Stock, Gregory, *Metaman: The Merging of Humans and Machines into a Global Superorganism*, New York, Simon & Schuster, 1993

Susruta, *Susrutasamhita*, Sastri, Ambikadatta, editor, Benares, Chowkhamba Sanskrit Series Office, 1954

Thompson, Douglas, Baby, can you hear me? *London Daily News*, April 1985

Thompson, William Irwin, *Coming into Being: Artifacts and Texts in the Evolution of Consciousness*, New York, St. Martin's, 1996

Thompson, William Irwin, *Transforming History: A Curriculum for Cultural Evolution*, Hudson, New York, Lindisfarne Books, 2001

Tiger, Lionel, *Optimism: The Biology of Hope*, New York, Simon & Schuster, 1979

Trivers, Robert L., Irven Devore interview, *Omni*, June 1993

Trivers, Robert L., *Social Evolution*, Menlo Park, California, Benjamin/Cummings, 1985

Tudge, Colin, *The Time Before History*, New York, Scribner, 1996

Van de Carr, René, *While You Are Expecting: Your Own Prenatal Classroom*, Atlanta, Humanics Press, 1997 (revision of *Prenatal Classroom*, Atlanta, Humanics Press, 1992)

Verny, Thomas, and Kelly, John, *The Secret Life of the Unborn Child*, New York, Summit Book, 1981

Weinberg, Steven, The revolution that didn't happen, *New York Review of Books*, October 1998

Wells, H. G., *An Outline of History*, New York, Macmillan, 1920

Wheelis, Allen, *On Not Knowing How to Live*, New York, Harper & Row, 1975

Wilson, David Sloan, and Sober, Elliott R., *Unto Others: The Evolution and Psychology of Unselfish Behavior*, Cambridge, Harvard University, 1997

Wilson, Edward O., *Sociobiology: The New Synthesis*, Cambridge, Harvard University, 1975

Winner, Ellen, *Gifted Children: Myths and Realities*, New York, BasicBooks, 1996

Wolpert, Lewis, *The Triumph of the Embryo*, New York, Oxford University, 1991

Woodley, R., Want to raise a genius? *People*, August 1982

Wright, Robert, *Nonzero: The Logic of Human Destiny*, New York, Pantheon, 2000

Youcha, G., Life before birth, *Science Digest*, December 1982

Zackheim, Michele, *Einstein's Daughter: The Search for Lieserl*, New York, Berkeley Publishing Group, 2000

Selected technical references citing the author's prenatal enrichment research

*Website **www.babyplus.com** contains several of the articles listed below; congress and conference presentations are available on audiocassette from the sponsoring organizations.*

Clinical report, *Hospital Doctor*, April 1990

Gifted babies, *Malaysian Doctor*, September 1994

Lazarev, M., A controlled assessment of fetal sonic stimulation comparing music and cardiac progressions, 1992-2001, *International Journal of Prenatal and Perinatal Psychology and Medicine*, volume 14, 2002

Logan, B., Biological measurements of prenatal stimulation, *Prenatal Perception, Learning and Bonding*, Blum, T., editor, Berlin, Leonardo Publishers, 1993

Logan, B., The cardiac curriculum: learning before birth, First Developmental Enrichment Conference of the Infant Stimulation Education Association, University of California at Los Angeles and Georgetown University, Costa Mesa, California, 1986

Logan, B., Clinical aspects of neurogenetic enrichment, medical faculty presentation, Moscow University, Moscow, Russia, 1994

Logan, B., A comparative evaluation of prenatally stimulated children, Fifth International Congress on Pre and Perinatal Psychology, Atlanta, 1991

165

Logan, B., Editorial letter, *Pre and Perinatal Psychology Journal*, volume 2, 1987

Logan, B., Fetal education forum, Fourth International Congress on Pre and Perinatal Psychology, University of Massachusetts, Amherst, 1989

Logan, B., Fetal sonic stimulation, *The Royal College of General Practitioners Official Reference Book*, London, Sterling Publications, 1995

Logan, B., Fetal speciators: the neurogenetic feedback hypothesis, *International Journal of Prenatal and Perinatal Psychology and Medicine*, volume 14, 2002

Logan, B., Infant outcomes of a prenatal stimulation pilot study, Fourth International Congress on Pre and Perinatal Psychology, University of Massachusetts, Amherst, 1989

Logan, B., Infant outcomes of a prenatal stimulation pilot study, *Pre and Perinatal Psychology Journal*, volume 6, 1991

Logan, B., *Neurogenetic Effects of Sonic Imprinting: An In Utero Curriculum for Improving Postnatal Performance*, Prenatal Institute, Seattle, 1990

Logan, B., Neurogenetic enrichment: from tradition to technology, New Technologies in Prenatology Conference, Naberezhny Chelny, Tartarstan, Russia, 1998

Logan, B., Neurogenetic optimization, First International Conference on Prenatal Learning and Bonding, Valencia, Spain, 1992

Logan, B., Prelearning: trials and trends, *International Journal of Prenatal and Perinatal Studies*, volume 4, 1992

Logan, B., Prenatal stimulation: an ancient practice updated, staff presentation, Shanxi Maternity Hospital, Taiyuan, China, 1992

Logan, B., Project Prelearn: the efficacy of in utero teaching, *International Journal of Prenatal and Perinatal Studies*, volume 1, 1989

Logan, B., Project Prelearn: the efficacy of in utero teaching, Ninth International Congress on Prenatal and Perinatal Psychology and Medicine, Jerusalem, 1989

Logan, B., Sonic stimulation of the unborn child: an evolutionary response to environmental challenge, faculty presentation, Madras Medical University, Madras, India, 1996

Logan, B., A special start: the extraordinary promise of prenatal learning, *Pre and Perinatal Psychology News*, 1989

Logan, B., A special start: the extraordinary promise of prenatal learning, Second Prenatal Education Symposium of the National Association for Prenatal Education, Saint-Raphäel, France, 1988

Logan, B., Teaching the unborn: precept and practice, *Pre and Perinatal Psychology Journal*, volume 2, 1987

Logan, B., The ultimate preventive: prenatal stimulation, Eighth International Congress on Prenatal and Perinatal Psychology and Medicine, Badgastein, Austria, 1986

Logan, B., The ultimate preventive: prenatal stimulation (excerpts), *Prenatal and Perinatal Psychology and Medicine: Encounter With the Unborn*, Fedor-Freybergh, P. G., and Vogel, M. L. V., editors, Carnforth, UK, Parthenon, 1988

Ridgway, R., A heartbeat away from blissful birth, *Doctor*, volume 7, 1990

Other selected technical references

Aoki, C., and Siekevitz, P., Plasticity in brain development, *Scientific American*, volume 259, 1988

Arulkumaran, S., Skurr, B., Tong, H., Kek, L. P., Yeoh, K. H., and Ratnam, S. S., No evidence of hearing loss due to fetal acoustic stimulation test, *Obstetrics & Gynecology*, volume 78, 1991

Arulkumaran, S., Talbert, D., Hsu, T. S., Chua, S., Anandakumar, C., and Ratnam, S. S., In-utero sound levels when vibroacoustic stimulation is applied to the maternal abdomen: an assessment of the possibility of cochlea damage in the fetus, *British Journal of Obstetrics and Gynaecology*, volume 99, 1992

Aslin, R. N., Pisoni, D. B., and Jusczyk, P. W., Auditory development and speech perception in infancy, *Handbook of Child Development*, Mussen, P. H., editor, New York, John Wiley, volume 2, 1983

Barasch, R. H., The infant curriculum--a concept for tomorrow, *Exceptional Infant*, Seattle, Special Child Publications, 1967

Barinaga, M., The anatomy of learning, *Science*, volume 274, 1996

Bench, R. J., and Anderson, J. H., Sound transmission to the human fetus through the maternal abdominal wall, *Journal of Genetic Psychology*, volume 113, 1968

Benjamin, J., Li, L., Patterson, C., Greenberg, B. D., Murphy, D. L., and Hamer, D. H., Population and familial association between the D4 dopamine receptor gene and measures of Novelty Seeking, *Nature Genetics*, volume 12, 1996

Blum, T., Early prenatal perception and adequate auditive stimulation, *International Journal of Prenatal and Perinatal Studies*, volume 3, 1991

Blum, T., editor, *Prenatal Perception, Learning and Bonding*, Berlin, Leonardo Publishers, 1993

Boddy, J., Information processing and functional systems in the brain, *Physiological Correlates of Human Behaviour*, Gale, A. and Edwards, J. A., editors, New York, Academic Press, 1983

Brooksbank, B. W. L., and Balázar, R., Aspects of the biochemical development of the brain, *Clinics in Developmental Medicine*, 77/78, Connelly, K. J., and Prechtl, H. F. R., editors, Philadelphia, Lippincott, volume 80, 1981

Buder, E. H., Lynch, M. P., and Oller, D. K., Phrasing in prelinguistic vocalizations, *Developmental Psychobiology*, volume 28, 1996

Busnell, M.-C., Granier-Deferre, C., and Lecanuet, J. P., Fetal audition, *Annals of the New York Academy of Sciences*, volume 662, 1992

Capute, A. J., Palmer, F. B., Shapiro, B. K., Wachtel, R. C., Schmidt, S., and Ross, A., Clinical linguistic and auditory milestone scale: prediction of cognition in infancy, *Developmental Medicine & Child Neurology*, volume 28, 1986

Caspi, A., Moffitt, T. E., and Silva, P. A., Are some people crime-prone? Replications of the personality-crime relationship across countries, genders, races, and methods, *Criminology*, volume 32, 1994

Caspi, A., and Silva, P. A., Temperamental qualities at age three predict personality traits in young adulthood: longitudinal evidence from a birth cohort, *Child Development*, volume 66, 1995

Chabris, C. F., Prelude or requiem for the "Mozart Effect"? *Nature*, volume 400, 1999

Changeux, J.-P., and Danchin, A., Selective stabilization of developing synapses as a mechanism for the specifications of a neuronal network, *Nature*, volume 264, 1976

Cheour, M., Martynova, O., Näätänen, R., Erkkola, R., Sillanpää, M., Kero, P., Raz, A., Kaipio, M.-L., Hiltanen, J., Aaltonen, O., Savela, J., and Hämäläinen, H., Speech sounds learned by sleeping newborns, *Nature*, volume 415, 2002

Chorney, M. J., Chorney, K., Seese, N., Owen, M. J., Daniels, J., McGuffin, P., Thompson, L. A., Detterman, D. K., Benbow, C., Lubinski, D., Eley, T., and Plomin, R., A quantitative trait locus associated with cognitive ability in children, *Psychological Science*, volume 9, 1998

Chugani, H. T., Development of regional brain glucose metabolism in relation to behavior and plasticity, *Human Behavior and the Developing Brain*, Dawson, G., and Fischer, K. W., editors, New York, Guilford, 1994

Chun, J. J., Nakamura, M. J., and Shatz, C., Transient cells of the developing mammalian telencephalon are peptide-immunoreactive neurons, *Nature*, volume 325, 1987

Cowan, W. M., Neuronal death as a regulative mechanism in the control of cell number in the nervous system, *Development and Aging in the Nervous System*, Rockstein, M., editor, New York, Academic Press, 1973

Cunningham, T. J., Naturally occurring neuron death and its regulation by developing neural pathways, *International Review of Cytology*, volume 74, 1982

Davidson, E. H., *Gene Activity in Early Development*, New York, Academic Press, 1976

DeCasper, A. J., and Fifer, W. P., Of human bonding: newborns prefer their mothers' voices, *Science*, volume 208, 1980

DeCasper, A. J., and Sigafoos, A. D., The intrauterine heartbeat: a potent reinforcer for newborns, *Infant Behavior & Development*, volume 6, 1983

DeCasper, A. J., and Spence, M., Prenatal maternal speech influences human newborn's auditory preferences, *Infant Behavior & Development*, volume 9, 1986

Detterman, D. K., The effect of heartbeat sound on neonatal crying, *Infant Behavior and Development*, volume 1, 1978

Devlin, B., Daniels, M., and Roeder, K., The heritability of IQ, *Nature*, volume 388, 1997

Diamond, M. C., Johnson, R. E., and Ingham, C., Brain plasticity induced by environment and pregnancy, *International Journal of Neuroscience*, volume 2, 1971

Dobbing, J., Human brain development and its vulnerability, *Biologic and Clinical Aspects of Brain Development*, Mead-Johnson Symposium on Perinatal and Developmental Medicine, volume 6, 1974

Dobbing, J., and Sand, J., The quantitative growth and development of the human brain, *Archives of Diseases in Childhood*, volume 48, 1973

Ebstein, R. P., Novick, O., Umansky, R., Priel, B., Osher, Y., Blaine, D., Bennett, E. R., Nemanov, L., Katz, M., and Belmaker, R. H., Dopamine D4 receptor (D4DR) exon III polymorphism associated with the human personality trait of Novelty Seeking, *Nature Genetics*, volume 12, 1996

Eccles, J. C., *The Neurophysiological Basis of Mind*, Oxford, Clarendon, UK, 1953

Eckerman, C. O., Oehler, J. M., Medvin, M. B., and Hannan, T. E., Premature newborns as social partners before term age, *Infant Behavior and Development*, volume 17, 1994

Eriksson, P. S., Perfilieva, E., Bjork-Eriksson, Thomas, Alborn, A.-M., Nordborg, C., Peterson, D. A., and Gage, F. H., Neurogenesis in the adult human hippocampus, *Nature Medicine*, volume 4, 1998

Evan, G. I., Life after death: why programmed suicide of cells is vital, *Science Spectra*, volume 3, 1996

Fedor-Freybergh, F., and Vogel, M. L. V., *Prenatal and Perinatal Psychology and Medicine: Encounters with the Unborn*, Carnforth, UK, Parthenon, 1988

Fifer, W. P., and Moon, C., Auditory experience in the fetus, *Behavior of the Fetus*, Smotherman, W. P., and Robinson, S. R., editors, Telford, UK, Caldwell, 1988

Fisch, R. O., Bilek, M. K., Horrobin, J. M., and Change, P. N., Children with superior intelligence at 7 years of age: a prospective study of the perinatal, medical and socioeconomic factors, *American Journal of Diseases of Children*, volume 1130, 1976

Forbes, H. S., and Forbes, H. B., Fetal sense reactions: hearing, *Journal of Comparative Psychology*, volume 7, 1927

Freeman, M., Is infant learning egocentric or duocentric? Was Piaget wrong? *Pre and Perinatal Psychology Journal*, volume 2, 1987

Gasser, T., Von Lucadou-Müller, I., Verleger, R., and Bacher, P., Correlating EEG and IQ: a new look at an old problem using computerized EEG parameters, *Electroencephalography and Clinical Neurophysiology*, volume 55, 1983

Gelman, S. R., Wood, S., Spellacy, W. N., and Abrams, R. M., Fetal movement in response to sound stimulation, *American Journal of Obstetrics and Gynecology*, volume 114, 1982

Gerhardt, K. J., and Abrams, R. M., Fetal hearing: characterizations of the stimulus and response, *Seminars in Perinatology*, volume 20, 1996

Gottlieb, G., Conceptions of prenatal development: behavioral embryology, *Psychological Review*, volume 83, 1976

Gould, E., Neurogenesis in adulthood: a possible role in learning, *Trends in Cognitive Sciences*, volume 3, 1999

Grier, J. B., Counter, S. A., and Shearer, W. M., Prenatal auditory imprinting in chickens, *Science*, volume 155, 1967

Grimwade, J., Walker, D., Bartlett, M., Gordon, S., and Wood, C., Human fetal heartrate change and movement in response to sound and vibration, *American Journal of Obstetrics and Gynecology*, volume 109, 1971

Hamburger, V., and Levi-Montalcini, R., Proliferation, differentiation, and degeneration in the spinal ganglia of the chick embryo under normal and experimental conditions, *Journal of Experimental Zoology*, volume 111, 1949

Hamburger, V., and Oppenheim, R. W., Naturally occurring neuronal death in vertebrates, *Neuroscience Commentary*, volume 1, 1982

Harvey, P. H., and Partridge, L., Evolutionary ecology: different routes to similar ends, *Nature*, volume 392, 1998

Hebb, D. O., *The Organization of Behavior: A Neuropsychological Theory*, New York, Harper & Row, 1949/1961

Hediger, M. L., Overpeck, M. D., Kuczmarski, R. J., McGlynn, A., Maurer, K. R., and Davis, W. W., Muscularity and fatness of infants and young children born small- or large-for-gestational age, *Pediatrics*, volume 102, 1998

Henshall, W. R., Intrauterine sound levels, *American Journal of Obstetrics and Gynecology*, volume 112, 1972

Hepper, P. G., An examination of foetal learning before and after birth, *Irish Journal of Psychology*, volume 12, 1991

Hepper, P. G., editor, Comparative studies of prenatal learning and behaviour: a special issue of the *Quarterly Journal of Experimental Psychology*, 1992

Hepper, P. G., Fetal psychology: an embryonic science, *Fetal Behaviour: Developmental and Perinatal Aspects*, Nijhuis, J. G., editor, New York, Oxford University, 1992

Hepper, P. G., Foetal learning: implications for psychiatry? *British Journal of Psychiatry*, volume 155, 1989

Hepper, P. G., and Leader, L. R., Fetal habituation, *Fetal and Maternal Medicine Review*, volume 8, 1996

Hepper, P. G., White, R., and Shahidullah, S., The development of fetal responsiveness to external auditory stimulation, *British Psychological Society Abstracts,* 1991

Hess, E. H., Imprinting, *Science*, volume 130, 1959

Hess, E. H., *Imprinting: Early Experience and the Developmental Psychobiology of Attachment*, New York, Van Nostrand, 1973

Huttenlocher, P. R., Synaptogenesis in human cerebral cortex, *Human Behavior and the Developing Brain*, Dawson, G., and Fischer, K. W., editors, New York, Guilford, 1994

Jacobson, M., *Developmental Neurobiology*, New York, Plenum, 1991

Jacobson, M., A plenitude of neurons, *Studies on the Development of Behavior and the Nervous System*, Gottlieb, G., editor, New York, Academic Press, volume 2, 1974

Jenny, H., *Cymatics*, Basel, Basilius, 1967

Kalil, R. E., Synapse formation in the developing brain, *Scientific American*, volume 261, 1989

Kerr, J., Wyllie, A., and Currie, A., Apoptosis: a basic biological phenomenon with wide-ranging implications in tissue kinetics, *British Journal of Cancer*, volume 26, 1972

Kisilevsky, B. S., Muir, D. W., and Lowe, J. A., Human fetal responses to sound as a function of stimulus intensity, *Obstetrics and Gynecology*, volume 73, 1989

Kiyono, S., Seo, M. L., Shibagki, M., and Inouye, M., Facilitative effects of maternal environmental enrichment on maze learning in rat offspring, *Physiology & Behavior*, volume 34, 1985

Kolata, G., Studying learning in the womb, *Science*, volume 225, 1984

Kraus, N., McGee, T. J., Carrell, T. D., Zecker, S. G., Nicol, T. G., and Koch, D. B., Auditory neurophysiologic. responses and discrimination deficits in children with learning problems, *Science*, volume 273, 1996

Krueger, R. F., Schmutte, P. S., Caspi, A., Moffitt, T. E., Campbell, K., and Silva, P. A., Personality traits are linked to crime among men and women: evidence from a birth cohort, *Journal of Abnormal Psychology*, volume 103, 1994

Kumin, I., *Pre-Object Relatedness: Early Attachment and the Psychoanalytic Situation*, New York, Guilford, 1995

Kuo, Z.-Y., *The Dynamics of Behavior Development*, New York, Plenum, 1976

Libet, B., Unconscious cerebral initiative and the role of conscious will in voluntary action, *Behavioral and Brain Sciences*, volume 4, 1985

Liley, A. W., The foetus as a personality, *Australia and New Zealand Journal of Psychiatry*, volume 6, 1972

Llinás, R. R., The intrinsic electrophysiological properties of mammalian neurons: insights into central nervous system function, *Science*, volume 242, 1988

Luz, N. P., Lima, C. P., Luz, S. H., and Felders, V. L., Auditory evoked response of the human fetus, *Acta Obstetrics-Gynecology Scandavica*, volume 59, 1980

Lykken, D., and Tellegen, A., Happiness is a stochastic phenomenon, *Psychological Sciences*, volume 7, 1996

Lynam, D., Moffitt, T., and Stouthamer-Loeber, M., Explaining the relation between IQ and delinquency: class, race, test motivation, school failure, or self-control? *Journal of Abnormal Psychology*, volume 102, 1993

Lynch, M. P., Oller, D. K., and Umbel, V., Onset of speech-like vocalizations in infants with Down syndrome, *American Journal of Mental Retardation*, volume 100, 1995

Miller, R. W., and Slot, W. J., Small head size after in utero exposure to radiation, *Lancet*, volume 2, 1972

Mistretta, C. M., and Bradley, R. M., Effects of early sensory experience on brain and behavioral development, *Studies on the Development of Behavior and the Nervous System*, Gottlieb, G., editor, New York, Academic Press, volume 4, 1978

Montan, S., Arulkumaran, S., Nyman, M., and Ratnam, S. S., Vibroacoustic stimulation does not alter the duration of high and low fetal heart rate variability episodes, *Journal of Perinatal Medicine*, volume 20, 1992

Montan, S., Arulkumaran, S., and Ratnam, S. S., Computerised cardiotocography following vibro-acoustic stimulation, *Journal of Perinatal Medicine*, volume 20, 1992

Murooka, H., Koie, Y., and Suda, N., Analyse des sons intrauterins et leurs effets tranquillisants sur le nouveau-né, *Journal of Obstetrics and Biological Reproduction*, volume 5, 1976

Nakae, K., A historical study on the thought of *taikyo*, *Japanese Journal of Education Research*, volume 50, 1983

Neher, A., Auditory driving observed with scalp electrodes in normal subjects, *Electroencephalography and Clinical Neurophysiology*, volume 13, 1961

Nyman, M., Arulkumaran, S., Hsu, T. S., Ratnam, S. S., Till, O., and Westgren, M., Vibroacoustic stimulation and intrauterine sound pressure levels, *Obstetrics & Gynecology*, volume 78, 1991

Nyman, M., Barr, M., and Westgren, M., A four-year follow-up of hearing and development in children exposed in utero to vibro-acoustic stimulation, *British Journal of Obstetrics and Gynaecology*, volume 99, 1992

Olds, C., Fetal response to music, *Pre and Perinatal Psychology Association of North America News*, April 1984

Oppenheim, R. W., Naturally occuring cell death during neural development, *Trends in Neuroscience*, volume 8, 1985

Oppenheim, R. W., Neuronal cell death and some related regressive phenomena during neurogenesis: a selective historical review and a progress report, *Studies in Developmental Neurobiology: Essays in Honor of Viktor Hamburger*, Cowan, W. M., editor, New York, Oxford University, 1981

Oppenheim, R. W., Ontogenetic adaptation and retrogressive processes in the development of the nervous system and behaviour: a neuroembryological perspective, *Clinics in Developmental Medicine*, 77/78, Connolly, K. J., and Prechtl, H. F. R., editors, Philadelphia, Lippincott, volume 80, 1981

Panthuraamphorn, C., Prenatal infant stimulation program, *Prenatal Perception, Learning and Bonding*, Blum, T., editor, Berlin, Leonardo Publishers, 1993

Peiper, A., *Cerebral Influence in Infancy and Childhood*, New York, Consultants Bureau, 1963

Peiper, A., Sinnesempfindungen des kindes vor seiner geburt, *Monatsschrift fur Kinderheilkunde*, volume 29, 1925

Prechtl, H. F. R., The study of neural development as a perspective of clinical problems, *Clinics in Developmental Medicine*, 77/78, Connolly, K. J., and Prechtl, H. F. R., editors, Philadelphia, Lippincott, volume 80, 1981

Preuss, T., and Gilly, W. F., Role of prey-capture experience in the development of the escape response in the squid *Loligo opalescens*: a physiological correlate in an identified neuron, *Journal of Experimental Biology*, volume 203, 2000

Purves, D., *Principles of Neural Development*, Sunderland, Massachusetts, Sinauer Associates, 1985

Querleu, D., Renard, X., Boutteville, C., and Crepin, G., Hearing by the human fetus? *Seminars in Perinatology*, volume 13, 1989

Querleu, D., Renard, X., and Crepin, G., Auditory perception and fetal reaction to sound stimulation, *Journal of Gynecological Obstetrics and Biological Reproduction*, volume 10, 1981

Querleu, D., Renard, X., Versyp, F., Paris-Delrue, L., and Crepin, G., Fetal hearing, *European Journal of Obstetrics and Gynecology and Reproductive Biology*, volume 2, 1988.

Rakic, P., Limits of neurogenesis in primates, *Science*, volume 227, 1985

Rakic, P., Local circuit neurons, *Neuroscience Research Progress Bulletin*, volume 13, 1975

Ramón y Cajal, S., Etude sur la neurogenèse de quelques vertébrés, translated by Guth, L., *Studies on vertebrate neurogenesis*, Springfield, Illinois, Thomas, 1929/1960

Rauscher, F. H., Shaw, G. L., Levine, L. S., Wright, E. L., Dennis, W. R., and Newcomb, R. L., Music training causes long-term enhancement of preschool children's spatial-temporal reasoning, *Neurological Research*, volume 19, 1997

Ray, W. S., A preliminary report on a study of foetal conditioning, *Child Development*, volume 3, 1932

Richards, M., Hardy, R., Kuh, D., and Wadsworth, M.E.J., Birth weight and cognitive function in the British 1946 cohort: longitudinal population based study, *British Medical Journal*, Volume 322, 2000

Rigatto, H., Moore, M., and Cates, D., Fetal breathing and behavior measured through a double-wall Plexiglas window in sheep, *Journal of Applied Physiology*, volume 61, 1986

Rimland, B. R., Savant capabilities of autistic children and their cognitive implications, *Cognitive Defects in the Development of Mental Illness*, Serban, G., editor, New York, Brunner/Mazel, 1978

Rosen, M. G., and Scibetta, J., Documenting human fetal EEG during birth, *Electroencephalography and Clinical Neurophysiology*, volume 27, 1969

Saffran, J. R., Aslin, R. N., and Newport, E. L., Statistical learning by 8-month-old infants, *Science,* volume 274, 1996

Salk, L., The effects of normal heartbeat sound on the behavior of the new-born infant: implications for mental health, *World Mental Health*, volume 2, 1960

Salk, L., Mother's heartbeat as an imprinting stimulus, *Transactions of the New York Academy of Sciences*, volume 24, 1962

Salk, L., Thoughts on the concept of imprinting and its place in early human development, *Canadian Psychiatric Association Journal*, volume 11, 1966

Sarnat, H. B., *Cerebral Dysgenesis: Embryology and Clinical Expression,* New York, Oxford University, 1992

Schlaug, G., Jancke, L., Huang, X., and Steinmetz, H., In vivo evidence of structural brain assymetry in musicians, *Science*, volume 267, 1995

Schwartz, F. J., Perinatal stress reduction, music, and medical cost savings, *Journal of Prenatal and Perinatal Psychology and Health*, volume 12, 1997

Shear, J., editor, *Explaining consciousness: the hard problem*, Cambridge, Massachusetts Institute of Technology, 1997

Shetler, D. J., The inquiry into prenatal musical experience: a report of the Eastman project 1980-87, *Pre and Perinatal Psychology Journal*, volume 3, 1986

Shindler, K. M., A three year study of fetal auditory imprinting, *Journal of the Washington Academy of Sciences*, volume 74, 1984

Skinner, B. F., *The Behavior of Organisms*, New York, Appleton-Century-Crofts, 1938

Sontag, L. W., and Wallace, R. F., Implications of fetal behavior and environment for adult personalities, *Annals of the New York Academy of Sciences*, volume 134, 1966

Sontag, L. W., and Wallace, R. F., The movement response of the human fetus to sound stimuli, *Child Development*, volume 6, 1935

Spelt, D. K., The conditioning of the human fetus in utero, *Journal of Experimental Psychology*, volume 38, 1948

Spencer, J. A. D., Deans, A., Nicolaidis, P., and Arulkumaran, S., Fetal heart rate response to vibroacoustic stimulation during low and high fetal heart rate variability episodes in late pregnancy, *American Journal of Obstetrics and Gynecology*, volume 165, 1991

Thompson, D. W., *On Growth and Form*, Cambridge, UK, Cambridge University Press, 1942, 1961 (abridged), New York, Dover, 1992

Treffert, D. A., The idiot savant: a review of the syndrome, *American Journal of Psychiatry*, volume 5, 1988

Trivers, R. L., The evolution of reciprocal altruism, *Quarterly Review of Biology*, volume 46, 1971

Turkewitz, G., and Kenny, P. A., Limitations on input as a basis for neural organization and perceptual development: a preliminary theoretical statement, *Developmental Psychobiology*, volume 4, 1982

Uttley, A. M., *Informational Transmission in the Nervous System*, London, Academic Press, 1979

Van de Carr, F. R., Fetal stimulation: videotaped outcomes, presentation at the Merritt Peralta Health Education Conference on Prenatal and Infant Stimulation, Oakland, 1985

Van de Carr, F. R., The Prenatal University, presentation at the Second International Congress on Pre and Perinatal Psychology, San Diego, 1985

Van de Carr, F. R., and Lehrer, M., Enhancing early speech, parental bonding and infant physical development using prenatal intervention in standard obstetric practice, *Pre and Perinatal Psychology Journal*, volume 1, 1986

Van de Carr, F. R., and Lehrer, M., Prenatal University: commitment to fetal-family bonding and strengthening of the family unit as an education institution, *Pre and Perinatal Psychology Journal*, volume 2, 1988

Van de Carr, K., Van de Carr, F. R., and Lehrer, M., Effects of a prenatal intervention program, *Prenatal and Perinatal Psychology and Medicine: Encounter With the Unborn*, Fedor-Freybergh, P. G., and Vogel, M. L. V., editors, Carnforth, UK, Parthenon, 1988

Walker, D., Grimwade, J., and Wood, C., Intrauterine noise: a component of the fetal environment, *American Journal of Obstetrics and Gynecology*, volume 109, 1971

Walter V. J., and Walter, W. G., The central effects of rhythmic sensory stimulation, *Electroencephalography and Clinical Neurophysiology*, volume 1, 1949

Wechsler, D., *The Range of Human Capacities*, Baltimore, Williams and Wilkins, 1935

Weiss, P., Nervous system (neurogenesis), *The Analysis of Development*, Willier, B. H., Weiss, P., and Hamburger, V., editors, Philadelphia, Saunders, 1955

Weiss, P., *Principles of Development*, New York, Holt, 1939

Wickett, J. C., Vernon, P.A., and Lee, D. H., Relationships between factors of intelligence and brain volume, *Personality and Individual Differences*, volume 29, 2000

Wigglesworth, J. S., Brain development and the structural basis of perinatal brain damage, *Perinatal Brain Insult*, Mead-Johnson Symposium on Perinatal and Developmental Medicine, volume 7, 1980

Wilmut, I., Schnieke, A. E., McWhit, J., Kind, A. J., Campbell, K. H. S., Viable offspring derived from fetal and adult mammalian cells, *Nature*, volume 385, 1997

Glossary

Not all entries appear in the main text, but are included for resonance. Asterisks indicate terms originating with the author.

Adaptation--Response to an environmental change; modification of morphology, physiology, or behavior in an individual, assuring survival and reproduction fitness --which if collectively effective can foster speciation.

Adaptationism--The innate ability for organismic conformation to new conditions, and the evolutionary process by which this faculty became ubiquitous.

Afferent--Inbound conveyance, physiologically peripheral impulse movement to centers such as neurons.

Altruism--Deferring self-interest to that of another individual, group, or ideal; instinct, emotion, and cognition can be determining factors, but even strategic personal sacrifice may return rewards greater than overtly egoistic acts.

Alpha rhythm--Also known as the Berger wave after its 1929 discoverer, Hans Berger, German psychiatrist at the University of Jena; surface measurement of electrical activity in the brain while a subject is alert but relaxed and with eyes closed, averaging 10.2 hertz (cycles per second) for adults, one to two hertz upon birth (protoalpha rhythm or slow wave, marked by shallow amplitude).

Anecdote--A usually short, personal account of some occurence, scientifically considered slack proof for an hypothesis; this bias against subjective observation--which presumes objective standards exist apart from philosophic constructs (cf. Karl Popper's *Objective Knowledge*)-- runs counter to uncertainty principle inferences and the unadvertised fact that empirical evidence constitutes accumulated stories, usually cast numerically, despite credentialed reportage whose legitimacy reflects the dominant yet always provisional paradigm.

Apgar--Physical evaluation of the newborn at one and five minutes; this widespread scoring system, introduced by Virginia Apgar in 1953, assigns descriptive values of 1 to 10, with higher numbers representing the healthiest neonates. There is a close connection between the five-minute reading and neurological status at twelve months of age.

Apoptosis--Cell death.

Arborization--Dendritic branching taking place during the second brain growth spurt (from 18 weeks gestational age, continuing about two years).

Astrocyte--A neuroglial cell shaped like a star.

*Audiogene--See echo effect.

Auditory driving--Sonic wave fronts, impacting upon the nervous system, dampen other sensory input--though acting synesthetically--and reconfigure normal electrical rhythmicity in the brain to like patterns; if incrementally faster than standard protoalpha frequency in the fetus and of sufficient duration for imprinting, this synchronous effect upon neuronal firing rate will advance information-processing to more mature levels. By conferring survival value directly correlated with functional neurology, prolific cortical cell death at the close of full-term gestation can be moderated beneficially, thus reprogramming a genetic imperative. The phenomenon of sound as a governor of synaptic activity was detected from photic driving research.

Autism--Mental impairment exhibiting marked withdrawal from reality, obsessively delusional, self-centeredness in the extreme but without egoism; its origin may be prenatal.

Autonomic system--That part of the vertebrate's networked nerves which controls certain involuntary elements like the heart, intestines, glands, etc.

Axiom--A self-evident truth, or so accepted for the purpose of argument.

Axon--A neuronal extension which carries impulses from the cell, larger and less branched than its dendritic counterpart.

*BabyPlus--Fetal stimulation technology employing curricularized heartbeat variants for developmentally appropriate engagement of neurogenesis before its critical imprinting window shuts at full-term gestation's end, thereby strengthening formative mental circuitry to resist standard protobrain cell death; this earliest enrichment by sonic means produces lifetime gains across all human performance categories, substantially elevating cognitive, social, creative, and empathic skills. Broad cultural acceptance is based on role-modeling of exemplars and commercial availability throughout more affluent countries, with subsidized dispersal for developing regions. The author conceptualized his innovation in 1982, which then received theoretical grounding previous to pilot studies, and has at the time of this publication benefitted over 100,000 children worldwide from every economic environment. Controlled clinical trials have supported no other effective methodology or product, neither music, speech, nor abdominal massage. The latest model is oval-shaped, and contains the most advanced sonic patterns, their single-button selection observable on a small viewing screen. For a product brochure, retail locations, or purchasing options, contact:

The BabyPlus Company
301 East Carmel Drive
Building G, Suite 300-2
Carmel, Indiana 46032

Phone	**(800) 330-6944**
Phone	**(317) 815-1111**
Fax	**(317) 815-0041**
Website	**www.babyplus.com**
email	**management@babyplus.com**

Bitracking--The brain's ability to follow two stimuli at once, though consciousness focuses singularly; applicable before birth where fetal reaction can be completely independent of an environmental event evoking neurological response--with corresponding influence upon patterned electrical activity--imprinting being the classic instance. Prenatally, this phenomenon illustrates that classic habituation to a stimulus does not indicate lack of mental tracking.

Brain cell death--Standard but massive neuronal loss peaking about 39.5 weeks gestational age, substantially less so with adult seniority.

Brain growth spurt--Proliferation of neural material during early developmental stages, initially nerve bodies then fibers; for humans, the former process begins at eight weeks from conception and lasts about two months, succeeded by axonal and dendritic growth over two years.

Branching--See arborization.

Canon--A rule, code of laws, established principle; also an individual's collected works.

*Cardiac curriculum--First generation sonic program for the author's prenatal enrichment technology, based upon his 1982 realization that imprinted maternal heartbeat if sequenced in recognizable but increasingly complex patterns could, through the effect of auditory driving, engage as rudimentary data-processing the nascent brain before neurogenesis experiences normal yet nearly complete cell death concluding full-term gestation; by zerobasing this process upon the imprinted one-hertz general frequency of every resting mother's bloodpulse, storage and transmission of suitably accelerated quanta would advance developmental processes in the fetal protobrain. Later augmented by a cortically centered rationale placing emphasis on more rapid sound progressions as well as greater tonal variety.

Cardiogenesis--The human heart begins beating erratically at three weeks from conception, which coincides with the brain's origin, and is regularized a week later--faster early in term but averaging 135 counts per minute during gestation, about twice as rapid as the base rate for that of a resting adult.

Casimir effect--Something from nothing, a potential first cause lacking prior design. Quantum electrodynamics maintains that no vacuum is wholly void, instead featuring transient or virtual particles--like photons-- which materialize and vanish randomly; Dutch physicist Hendrik Casimir's 1948 proposal was verified in 1997 by Steve Lamoreaux at the Los Alamos National Laboratory.

Cell--The life package for self-replication, its outer membrane housing a nucleus which encapsulates genetic material-- heritable information and the particular developmental agenda; an easily visualized explanation from Richard Brennan's *Dictionary of Scientific Literacy*:

The nucleus of a cell is a library containing life's instructions. The chromosomes would be the bookshelves inside the library, the DNA would be individual books on each shelf, genes would be the chapters in each book, and the nucleotide bases making up the strands of DNA would be the words on the pages of the individual books.

Cell assembly--A diffuse neural structure which upon arousal acts briefly as an integrated, discrete system, facilitating other networks along with motor functions; triggered by like arrangements or sensory input--typically both--a series of its firings constitutes the phase sequence or thought process. This concept was proposed in 1946 by Canadian psychologist Donald O. Hebb.

Chromosome--Of linear or spherical assembly, a genetic strand in cell nuclei which transmits hereditary information.

Cladistics--A classification system noting speciational and evolutionary features.

Clinical Linguistic and Auditory Milestone Scale (CLAMS) The first infant assessment (birth to 24 months) correlating expressive and receptive abilities with later cognitive development; introduced in 1986 by Johns Hopkins University pediatricians under Arnold J. Capute.

Conditioning--Modification of behavior whereby a response formerly connected to one stimulus is associated with another.

*Conscious imprinting--Elementary and repetitious stimuli eliciting prenatal awareness like synchronized breathing or limb movement, which even if habituated through rudimentary cognizance continue to register neurologically; effective only during a crucial development period, the process commences approximate with the onset of fetal hearing and conclusion to the first brain growth spurt--about 16-18 weeks from conception--then ending once fear begins, at or soon after birth. Unlike later experience, this early form of learning evokes a lifetime response without causing anxiety.

Cortex--The outer layer of an organ or corporeal structure; while technically distinguishing that gray matter covering the mammalian cerebrum and cerebellum, adjectival usage can generally reference the entire brain.

*Cortical curriculum--In utero sonic stimulation progressing from the human protobrain's normative alpha rhythm of approximately one or two cycles per second to about half the adult standard (10.2 hertz), indigenously governed through auditory driving by maternal and fetal heartbeat rate; in the author's more recent prenatal enrichment technology, this frequency moves well beyond its cardiac rhythm predecessor.

Cutaneous--Relating to the skin.

Demography--Population science, the study of growth rate, age, and forces affecting these factors.

Dendrite--A nerve cell extension which receives impulses.

Differentiation--A developmental change to a more specific structure or function, predominantly applicable during early life.

Digital sampling device--Electronic converter of sound to binary signals which synthetically replicate their source.

Duocentric learning--Term and concept originating from Mac Freeman in 1987 to describe fetal awareness outside its own person, prompted by maternal bloodpulses surrounding the womb; this view opposes Jean Piaget's egocentric hypothesis, considering early consciousness suppressed after birth under an intrinsically selfish society.

*Echo effect--The perceived recurrence of sound no longer present: when clocks continue chiming past their actual cessation, music that has stopped reverberating but mentally lingers--the "haunting melody." Temporal patterns resonate in the brain according to neuronal firing congruent with cardiac rhythms imprinted prebirth; since from auditory driving these in utero stimuli generate nascent cognition detected electroencephalographically as protoalpha waves, they become the base matrix for every subsequent input configuration. "Ghost" sonic activity may register synesthetically, and has multisensory parallels like the afterimage or photogene (its counterpart here an *audiogene*). The first scientific notation of this phenomenon appears to be by Ulric Neisser, who called it "echoic memory."

Electroencephalography (EEG)--Cranial surface measurement of minute electrical activity in the brain; for all vertebrates, an alert state without visual stimulation produces alpha rhythm, which among prebirth or newborn humans manifests a slow state of one to two cycles per second (hertz)--arguably imprinted by maternal and fetal heartbeat--rising to 10.2 cycles per second at puberty, the adult rate.

Embryo--The first stage of life, in *Homo sapiens* beginning with conception and concluding eight weeks later.

Empathy--The deliberate or intuitive congruence of feeling with another's consciousness, enabling maximal communication and kinship.

Encephalization--A ratio describing brain-body growth; the encephalization quotient compares average animal size.

Engram--A postulated empirical alteration in the neuron which explains memory, contrasting less localized arguments.

Epigenesis--Development through differentiation, the genetic curriculum dependent for its expression upon external causes and events.

Eugenics--Hereditary innovation through controlled breeding, selective reproduction; racially misused to abhorrent result among *Homo sapiens*, and assailed with reasoned fervor by Gina Maranto in *Quest for Perfection*. Since human prenatal enrichment applies homogenously, this term's sole relevance in that context would be to democratic ends serving collective improvement--which redounds individually.

Fetus--After the embryonic stage, life's next phase; in humans it starts at eight weeks from conception and ends with birth.

Fitness landscape--Alternatively termed an adaptive terrain which maps ontogenetic differences, the abilities or behavior of individuals within a population ranked for their survival value (although this metaphor could describe civilizations, species). The concept was originally from Sewall Wright in 1931, then elaborated under Stuart Kauffman and Brian Goodwin; it is well explained by Daniel Dennett.

Flynn effect--Substantial gains in IQ throughout developed countries beginning with the mid-20th century, suggesting a macroevolutionary response to informational demands from increased cultural complexity; an observation by James R. Flynn, University of Otago, New Zealand.

192

Ganglion--Nerve tissue or neural group external to the brain proper or spinal cord; plural, ganglia.

Gene--Heredity's minion, segmented DNA inside a chromosome evolved for some unique function.

*Gifted Generation--Individuals enriched prebirth by curricularized variants in the in utero maternal bloodpulse, thus elevating cognitive skills and behavior for lifetime benefit to themselves, their family, and society; from this group's 1987 debut, a population of diverse socioeconomics numbering over 100,000 around the world has been achieved in little more than a decade.

Glial cell--Facilitative or helper tissue constituting lattices for migrating neurons in their developmental stages; plural, glia or neuroglia.

Gravida--A pregnant woman; plural, gravidae.

Habituation--Decreased response to a recurring stimulus. During the preconscious imprinting period, fetal reactivity takes place solely at the neurologic level; later, biochemical tracking of repeated input continues even during habituation, independent from physical effect. Paul Ehrlich's recent *Human Natures* is especially lucid on this subject.

Homeostasis--An equilibrous state between interdependent elements.

Hydrophone--A listening device whose operation is not impeded by moisture, thus functioning underwater or in utero.

Hypothesis--A conditionally verifiable proposition, but true to its time; an empirically testable subset of theory.

In vitro--External to the organism; in an artificial environment.

Idiot savant--An otherwise mentally impaired individual, usually autistic, with extraordinary if quite defined computational or creative talent; the derogatory prefix for this term is being eliminated.

Imprinting--The impact of a significant occurrence or simple, repeated stimulus in early life--almost entirely prenatal--not requiring reward, which permanently affects an organism without producing anxiety; the genetically programmed occasion for this elemental learning process in its preconscious phase evoking no behavioral response is coincidental with the first brain growth spurt (weeks 8-18 from conception), concluding the conscious stage once fear begins, at or just following birth, and cannot be altogether habituated even if overt fetal interest wanes.

Inhibitory neuron--Cortical provision for shutting down a cell assembly once transmission has taken place; the speed of return from an ignited to a latent state increases with cerebral complexity, an efficiency indicator which may be further evolved by prenatal enrichment.

Interoceptive sense--Receptors detecting stimuli from within the body, specifically the viscera.

Invagination--Infolding of cranial tissue as its proliferation encounters the skullcase; the resulting fissures, pronounced in *Homo sapiens*, serve as sites for highly active neural interface, putatively enhanced from curricularized sonic stimulation.

***Kitty Hawk singularity**--Sole proof, a threshold instance, generic changepoint, paradigm onset--after the 1903 first motored flight by the Wright brothers near North Carolina's village of the same name (actually launched from an adjacent Kill Devil Hill); nonetheless, while event, process, or behavior replication is technically redundant if qualitative change happens once under accurate observation, the reflective skepticism of science ever tempers its impulsive curiosity--objective evidence demands duplicates, empirical cloning.

Lamarckism--Hypothesis by French naturalist Jean Baptiste de Lamarck (1744-1829), long in scientific disfavor, that acquired characteristics are heritable; some contemporary researchers suggest reexamining certain aspects of this progressive postulate, especially since a new behavior can shape its environment hence reinforce the novelty through adaptive response.

Law--Under like conditions, an invariable relationship between or among phenomena.

*Law of neurogenetic potential--The degree of genetically fixed cell dieoff in the fetal brain (which limits all subsequent organismic output), transpiring massively for humans as the 39.5-week gestational age concludes, is substantially dependent upon earlier imprinting--stochastic or deliberate.

$$P_n = DI$$
$$D = fI$$

*Law of ontogenetic potential--An individual's ability is determined by genetic and environmental influences--including in humans the designed alongside random consequences of culture--contextual with its age.

$$P_o = \frac{G \quad E}{A}$$

*Law of phylogenetic potential--A species performs relative to the conglomerate prospect of its constituents--through

195

natural or cultural selection--in proportion with their number, an average ontogenetic praxis for the biomass; if this value substantially exceeds the former norm, achieving a critical state, displacement generates collective metamorphosis.

$$P_p = \frac{\sum_{1-1}^{N} \frac{N}{1-1} P_{o_1}}{B}$$

Limbic system--Mammalian deep brain structures central to emotion, motivation, and behavior, also affecting autonomic functions.

Macroevolution--Massive change producing new taxonomic groups, the engine of speciation; originally phrased "quantum evolution" by George Gaylord Simpson.

*Martyrdom equity--Priceless value for an optimally altruistic commodity, maximum gain through the ultimate sacrifice; whether measured in time, effort, or physical being itself, by contributing one's life to a cause which benefits others, personal reward better than any material, mental, or emotional alternative comes from the greatest empathic practice, existential if not spiritual purpose attained.

Morphogenesis--The developmental processes of an organism, including formation and differentiation.

Morphology--Structure, shape, size; externalities, not content--a physical, psychological, conceptual, or cultural measure.

Myelination--The sheathing of myelin, a soft white fatty substance, around nerve fibers; facilitates impulse transmission, therefore information-processing efficiency.

Nemo--A self-effacing principle added to the psychoanalytic cornerstones of id, ego, and superego, equating here with that further sentience which fetally enriched youth express; apart from Jules Verne's subaquatic Captain (also another recondite scientist in the present author's novel about prenatal stimulation, *Enigmata*), the term was first given a characterological meaning by John Fowles, *The Aristos*:

> The nemo is an evolutionary force, as necessary as the ego. The ego is uncertainty, what I am; the nemo is potentiality, what I am not.

Although Fowles interprets the nemo as limiting individuality--and, to his esthetic, therefore possessed of a dark side--an implicit empathy suggests its immediate context.

Neocortex--Province for the majority of neurons, gray matter comprising four major areas or lobes sharing many complex functions, the brain's outer, latest evolved layer, deeply folded with dense interfaces, among mammals best pronounced in man; consciousness centers, recognition, rational thinking, and language are its prominent features.

Neonatal--Newborn.

Neoteny--Retention of immature features into adulthood, notably characterizing various amphibians; also sexual maturity attained while still in the larval stage. For *Homo sapiens* this principle has profound meaning--an unusually extended childhood with similar prolongation of brain growth.

Neural tube--An infolding and fusion of tissue in vertebrate embryos, which becomes the brain.

197

Neuroblast--An embryonic ganglion cell.

Neurogenesis--Formation of nerve cells in the fetus.

*Neurogenetic enrichment--The fetal advantaging of brain development in general, but most effectively from curricularized sonic stimulation, promoting lifetime cognitive and behavioral benefits.

Neuron--The nervous system's primary unit in animals; nerve cells generate and transmit electrochemical impulses.

Neurotransmitter--Molecular secretions from axon terminals to nerve receptors, these signals bridging synaptic gaps.

Ontogene--The individual.

Ontogeny--An individual organism's development.

Overlaid function--Any derivative organic or cultural process: speaking a byproduct of respiration and ingestion, prenatal stimulation from indigenous cardiac imprinting, empathy born of cognition, artifacts as nature shaped for conscious ends, polis an extended family; its originating process is called *exaptation*.

*Pantomeme--The universal morphology of culture as depicted over time, how all artifacts--ideas and created objects-- derive from simpler predecessors, the curriculum called human history; epigenesis is the biochemical parallel.

Parturition--Birthing.

Pathogenesis--The origin or development of a disease.

Perinatal--During birth.

Postpartum--Following birth.

Postulate--An assumption, proposal, unproved assertion.

*Preconscious imprinting--The simplest, recurring stimuli register neurogenetically--before development of vertebrate awareness--thus elicit no behavioral response yet morphologically shape consciousness.

*Prelearner--An individual benefitted during neurogenesis from enrichment as a cultural practice, its influence optimized when in progressively sequenced sonic format.

*Prelearning--Prenatal learning--promoted most successfully by curricularized sound--which, from mitigative impact upon genetically mandated protobrain cell death at full-term gestation's end, endows newborns with a broader base for appreciating all subsequent experience; if bonobo chimpanzees can be trained for mortal thought processes and speak through technological assistance, then otherwise unrealizable potential among humans facing acute environmental niche challenges deserves no less access to performance liberation.

*Prelearning theory--Congruent in morphology with both fetal age and environment but incrementally compounded beyond standard complexity, sonic stimuli alter neurogenetic development whereby--from imprintable auditory driving which advances firing rates that have become culturally unresponsive--normative brain cell apoptosis centering on 39.5 weeks gestational age is significantly reduced; the consequences may include dendritic and axonal proliferation accompanied by advanced arborization or branching, accelerated differentiation, thicker myelinization, increased synaptic interface, neurotransmitter enhancement, more main and inhibitory neurons, glial cells, or astrocytes, hence endowing lifelong cognitive as well as behavioral boons. The author advanced this thesis in 1982.

Prenatal stimulation--Neurogenetic advantaging by sensory engagement, irrespective of fetal consciousness, to reduce through imprinted informational exercise protobrain cell death concurrent with full-term parturition; singularly persuasive when the stimuli are curricularized sounds, establishing permanent gains for all performance areas.

Principle--A fundamental truth, rule, or assumption.

Protobrain--Identified by Stanford University researchers in 1987, this fully functioning neurological structure addresses a vertebrate's earliest information management--signal receipt and transmission; with humans it atrophies substantially as normative gestation is completed, though playing an essential role for later cerebral development.

Protobrain cell death--Cataclysmic neuronal depopulation or dieoff in the fetal brain from excess production assuring minimal organismic competence for lifetime responsiveness to environmental requirements, therefore redundant only when not stimulated; genetically programmed in concert with developmental triggers, the cause is primarily epigenetic, secondarily stochastic-- hence open to influence. In humans initial brain growth peaks by gestational week 18, with its reduced extent-- variously estimated as a net loss reaching 50 to 90 percent of the original quantity--becoming inert gray and white matter. Cell death in the brain commences with neurogenesis and registers its prominence just before full-term birth, the morphology approximating a bell curve. Aside from ongoing but very minor hippocampal development in the dentate gyrus detected recently by Salk Institute researchers, no evidence exists that the resultant postnatal cell count is other than predominantly stable until normative or syndromic degeneration takes its toll during seniority.

Psychopathy--A mental disorder characterized by acute antisocial behavior, inordinate self-concern; reduced cranial circumference at birth correlates with major criminality--which includes a substantial psychopathic population--suggesting sustained impairment of cognitive hence performance choices due to diminished neurology, arguably countered through prenatal enrichment.

Real time analyzer--An electronic instrument which converts audio signals to a visual format, its frequency spectrum permitting sonic analysis.

Reciprocal altruism--Superficially cynical but at its core a pragmatically empathic concept suggested by Robert Trivers in 1971: Ego gains from reducing immediate or potential threats through accommodation, even mimicking charitability; elaborating Richard Dawkins' selfish genetics hypothesis, the net outcome of this opportunistic personal morality evolved as a group dynamic is that in time it synergistically elevates the institutional norm, an acquired trait transforming enhanced individual consciousness into collective conscience.

Reverse engineering--Building backwards, discovering function's purpose and cause from the resulting object or process; beloved methodology of political espionage, product piracy, and the scientific mind where perceptual bias can be diminished through zerobasing evolution's route to an observer--psychobiological dynamics.

Rule--A phylogenetically proscriptive action or behavior presuming permanence; also, the traditional method for solving problems.

Santiago theory--Alternative model of cognition to representational systems; advanced by Humberto Maturana and Francisco Varela in the 1970s at the University of Santiago. Opposing Plato's objectivism, their holistic thesis rejects the brain as processing independent information, instead considering it to be a contextual participant for any perceived event, therefore co-creative. Fritjof Capra sympathetically reviews this subject in *The Web of Life*.

Savantism--Phenomenal but usually isolated mathematical or artistic abilities describing individuals often autistically impaired; its source may be fetal, a 1987 postulation of the author reported in Darold Treffert's *Extraordinary People: Understanding "Idiot Savants."*

Selfish gene--Proposed by Richard Dawkins through his 1976 book of the same name, he maintains that life's sole function is selfpreservation with each organism relentlessly replicating its essence, the DNA program contained genetically; in conservatively defending ecological zones, however, these "survival machines" must employ considerable creativity against altered conditions or clever opponents, over time evolving stratagems of overt compromise which become pervasive, reciprocal altruism so transformative its practitioner assumes as substance the empathic morphology.

Serendipity--Beneficial encounter with the unsought.

Sinusoidal wave--A pattern of sine curve oscillation, this naturally fluctuating form includes cardiac rhythm;

electronically visualized by oscilloscope or real time analyzer.

Sociobiology--Behavior derives from a biologic base, its coordinates genetically transmitted and transformed by evolution; a principal exponent is Harvard zoologist Edward O. Wilson.

Stirpiculture--The breeding of pure stock, a term replaced by eugenics.

Stochastic--Involving chance, probability, or a random variable.

Striatum--A primordial brain section predating the cortex and limbic system, possible site of early noncognitive learning based on stimulus-response repetition; sensitive to form, not content.

Superbaby--Media pejorative for a child intensively stimulated after birth but not before, therefore at mercy of the same limitations--and reactions to pressured learning--as peers without this exposure; however, the fetally enriched (where protobrain cell death peaking at 39.5 weeks of gestational age has been minimized) extract more from the normative developmental environment, to permanent gain.

Superbaby syndrome--Lifelong condition deriving from early but strictly postnatal sensory overload of standard neurogenetic capacitance; children not prenatally stimulated exhibit immediate or, if first responding with promise, delayed resistance to excessive efforts by parents or programs, resulting in major psychological deficits.

Synapse--A junction where neuronal interaction occurs; across its cleft, chemical transmitters send impulses.

203

Syndrome--Abnormal symptomatology, but as a pattern of superlative aptitude or behavior may also describe the standard undergoing displacement.

Synesthesia--An effect produced by one sense as if it were another, e.g., sound for sight; imprinted prenatal sonic enrichment evokes patterns enhancing multisensory neural receptors for durable benefit.

Taikyo--Ancient Japanese art of fetal stimulation, with Chinese, Indian, and perhaps prehistoric precedence.

Theory--A system of explanatory assumptions about phenomena--substances, events, processes, behaviors, or thoughts; this propositional set may subsume conjectures that are subject to quantifiable measurement.

Transducer--A device translating power systems, such as electrical to acoustic energy; in auditory parlance, synonymous contextually with a sound speaker.

Viscera--Those internal organs of the body located in the trunk's cavity--heart, liver, intestines, etc.

*Winner Gives All--Reciprocal altruism--where advantage accrues through defensive default--can be tested with two excruciating strategems, the Prisoner's Dilemma and Tit for Tat; these are examined in *Social Evolution*, by Robert Trivers, while Daniel Dennett explores their philosophic implications (see *Darwin's Dangerous Idea*). But raising ethical stakes forces a player to realize that conscience shrinks unless what it most represents survives, ideal as artifact--created object, thought preserved, moral act . . . an inverse variant of the filmic message from 1983's *WarGames* ("the only winning move is not to play"), how Robert Wright concludes *Nonzero*: "...winning will depend on not wanting other peoples to lose." In forsaking everything except sacrifice for a person or principle, absolution among pervasive pain becomes possible, an existential art. Unlike those retributive contests above, this competition concludes as soon as begun, a gambit of one, since no consummately virtuous match may even commence unless an individual is pitted against their own self: The singular role cannot be usurped; challenge and change begin at home, through mental windows, before the heart's hearth, with every soul a threshold to the universe.

Zerobase--Originally a budgetary process pleasing parsimonious economists--to demonstrate minimal need or cost justification for expenditures--this approach can address any problem by reducing presuppositions as much as the dominant paradigm allows. Under such an austere thesis minimal observer influence increases chances of veracity (contrast subjectivism); nonetheless, as consciousness continues to evolve, the supplanting of personal interests by global, then cosmic, perhaps even multiversal knowledge and empathy suggests ever approaching-- though never attaining--the ultimate zerobase, where nothing equals infinity.

Index

abortion, 124
Abrams, R. M., 60
academic achievement, 31,
40, 93
adaptation, 58, 66, 127, 184
adaptationism, 184
alpha rhythm, 40, 85, 93,
100, 140, 184, 190, 191
Altman, Philip, 80
altruism, 33, 85, 126, 184
altruism, reciprocal, 38, 41,
201, 202, 204
Alzheimer's disease, 37, 122
Aoki, Chiye, 51
Apgar test, 27, 185
Apgar, Virginia, 185
apoptosis, 42, 46, 47, 49,
50, 55, 63, 66, 70, 72, 74,
81, 84, 95, 120, 185, 199
arborization, 52, 185, 187,
199
Archimedes, 87
Aristotle, 3, 139
arrhythmia, cardiac, 87
astrocyte, 185, 199
attention span, neonatal, 24,
25, 28
Auden, W.H., 129
audiocassette player,
portable, 16, 69, 123,
134, 141
audiogene, 185, 191
auditory driving, 80, 82, 85,
100, 103, 104, 133, 140,
188, 190, 191, 199
autism, 35, 122, 186

autonomic system, 12, 186
axon, 186, 198
BabyPlus, 103, 108, 113,
114, 116, 122, 123, 126,
186, 187
Baker, Robin, 10
Barkow, Jerome H., 66
Basalla, George, 120
Beatles, 16
Beecher, Henry Ward, 17
Bench, R. J., 59
Berger wave, 184
Berger, Hans, 184
Berman, Morris, 107
Big Bang, 49, 63, 98
bioengineering, 74
birth, 23, 24, 26
birth, breech, 23, 28, 110
birthweight, high, 27
birthweight, low, 28, 93
bitracking, 111, 187
blinking, 93
bloodpulse, maternal, 61,
62, 78, 79, 102, 108, 111,
112, 190, 193
bonding, 22, 113
Bothe, Helga, 69
Bradley, Robert, 55
Brahms, Johannes, 23, 76
brain, cell death, 42, 45, 53,
74, 96, 114, 133, 187,
188
brain, growth spurt, 11, 185,
187, 190, 194
brain, imaging, 100
brain, size, 36, 37, 159

208

209

210

213

Rex Rystedt

BIOGRAPHICAL NOTE

"A leading and revered expert in his field," according to *Executive Woman* of London, Brent Logan--director of Prenatal Institute in Seattle--is the highly acclaimed originator of a quantum advance in human development who brought its message to the vast populations of China, Russia, India, and Southeast Asia. Prompted by requests from parents everywhere, this vision is now available for anyone wishing to create a better future through nurturing greater opportunity during pregnancy.

Pursuing a suggestion from his late wife, Helga Bothe, since 1982 he has pioneered how best to enrich the fetus. His theoretical articles and clinical studies in academic journals initiated neurogenetic investigations which produced the only effective technology providing lifetime benefits for our next generation.

Reports about Brent Logan's discoveries appear regularly in the foremost publications and as television or radio features on national networks, already reaching a fascinated audience exceeding 500 million. His research has caught the attention of many prominent interests, from the education and medical communities to the corporate sector and governments.

After service as an army photojournalist in Germany, the author received graduate degrees before teaching at the university level, then headed international, multicultural, and social service programs for 15 years, working closely with dysfunctional adults, disadvantaged children, and the mentally ill. This background is strongly reflected in his writings about developmental psychology.

Founder of various applied research facilities, Brent Logan continues groundbreaking projects which enhance the natural evolution of *Homo sapiens* through cultural processes. When not speaking worldwide before professional groups or the public, he resides in the American Pacific Northwest with his wife, Karin Müller. Further information can be found at **www.brentlogan.net**.

217

Printed in the United States
1278800004BA/261